C000276766

ISLE OF ARRAN

A field guide for students of geology

by W. S. McKERROW and F. B. ATKINS

Edited by C. J. Lister

©THE GEOLOGISTS' ASSOCIATION

Second Edition, 1989

CONTENTS

LIST OF FIGURES

LIST OF EXCURSIONS

LIST OF PLATES (between pages 48 and 49)

Plate 1. The U-shaped valley of Glen Rosa in the Northern Granite mountains; and Cir Mhor (798m). The Witch's Step, the prominent notch in the skyline (half right), and the narrow gorge in the valley bottom represent the line of a dolerite dyke [Excursion 1].

Plate 2. Contact between the Garvock Group of the Lower Old Red Sandstone (left, south) and the Dalradian (right, north) in Glen Rosa [Excursion 1, locality 5].

Plate 3. Polymict conglomerate close to the Devonian/Carboniferous boundary at Corrie [Excursion 2, locality 1, bed e]. The clasts include vein quartz, quartzite, schist, sandstone, siltstone and andesite.

Plate 4. *Gigantoproductus* in the Corrie Limestone near Laggan Cottage [Excursion 3, locality 4]. Most of the valves are in the life position, convex sides facing downwards.

Plate 5. The basal Permian rocks on the north-east coast [Excursion 3, locality 12], consisting of interbedded wind-blown sands and parallel-sided flash-flood conglomerates.

Plate 6. King's cave, north of Drumadoon [Excursion 4, locality 14]; one of a series of old sea caves at the back of the Main Rock Platform, carved in dune-bedded Permian sandstones.

Plate 7. View from the north of the Drumadoon sill [Excursion 4, locality 9], a quartz-feldspar porphyry intrusion with well-developed columnar jointing. Its feeder dyke is exposed on the shore in the foreground [Excursion 4, locality 11].

Plate 8. Convoluted flow banding in a pitchstone intrusion on the Tormore shore [Excursion 4, locality 16].

Notes. The details of routes given in these guides do not imply a right of way. The onus of obtaining permission to use footpaths and to examine exposures rests on the user of the Guide who should carefully observe the Code for Geological Field Work, issued from the Librarian, The Geologists' Association, C/o Department of Geology, University College, Gower Street, London WC1E 6BT.

In particular, those in charge of parties should ensure that there is no indiscriminate hammering of, or collecting from, exposures and that no damage is caused to property.

Any information (eg. change in footpaths, filling in of quarries, threat to SSIs, new exposures) that would update and improve a revised edition of this Guide would be welcomed by the Association.

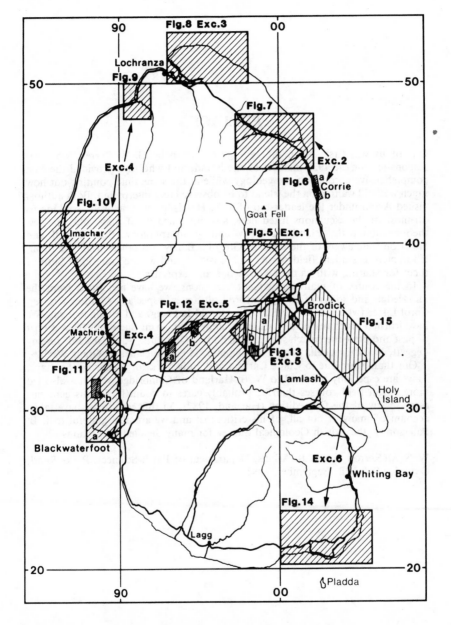

Figure 1: Key to the excursion maps (Figs. 5-15)

PREFACE

One of us was first shown the geology of Arran by G. W. Tyrrell, who was responsible for the 1928 memoir of the island, and who thus provided the first comprehensive account of the geology while at the same time pointing out how much was still waiting on the island to be observed and interpreted. Both authors visited Arran under the leadership of J. V. Harrison, who, as well as taking us on most of the excursions listed here, also informed us of many old and new theories about the island's geology and geomorphology. Both Tyrrell and Harrison were aware of the ideas of Gregory, Bailey and others who, like them, led numerous student field parties to the island, and we are grateful to both of them for sharing with us their knowledge and expertise.

In the course of many subsequent excursions, we have benefitted from the knowledge and ideas of many Oxford colleagues, especially Gordon Cressey, Carol Lister (who is also our Editor!), Harold Reading, and Hugh Jenkyns. We have learned much (especially sedimentology) from Ami Sneh and from a host of past and present research students, including Guy Plint, Alan Heward, Jeremy Leggett, Mark Burchell, Peter Cunningham, Hugh Sinclair and Grant Wach.

Our thanks are due to Claire Carlton and Julia York for preparing the maps.

We are especially indebted to W. B. Harland of Cambridge, who has also led more Arran field courses than he probably cares to count(!), for his generous essay review of the first edition (Harland, 1987) – in this edition we have taken account of many, if not all, of his criticisms; and we are also grateful to I. B. Paterson of the British Geological Survey for many detailed suggestions.

W. S. McKerrow and F. B. Atkins, Department of Earth Sciences, Parks Road, Oxford, OX1 3PR. September, 1988.

CHAPTER 1

INTRODUCTION

WHY ARRAN?

Why is Arran so popular for student geological field training? There are many reasons, but probably the foremost is the large variety of igneous and sedimentary rocks to be seen on the excellent coastal and inland exposures, perhaps excelling any other area of comparable size in the world.

The sedimentary rocks include representatives of most systems from the Cambrian to the Pleistocene, and their depositional environments range from deep marine to shallow marine, and from coal swamps to deserts. The igneous rocks include pillow basalts, sills and dykes of dolerite and quartz-feldspar-porphyry, the Northern Granite pluton and the collapsed caldera of the volcano that now forms the Central Ring Complex. Metamorphic rocks are represented by the Dalradian schists of northern Arran, and in the thermal aureoles of the larger intrusions.

Some of the variety of sedimentary and metamorphic rocks is related to the fact that Arran straddles the line of the Highland Boundary Fault. The Dalradian schists occur along strike from similar beds in the Grampian Highlands, while the younger beds in Arran are more comparable with those of the Midland Valley of Scotland. Its location on a major fault may also be why Arran is one of the major Palaeocene igneous centres in north-west Britain. Renewed movements may have occurred along old fault zones at a time when the North Atlantic was starting to open between Europe and Greenland. Study of the geological map of Scotland will show that many of the Tertiary igneous centres lie on, or close to, large faults.

There were many times when the Scottish Highlands were uplifted with respect to the Midland Valley; some of Arran's geological history can be worked out by a study of pebbles in conglomerates in conjunction with deductions about the depositional environments in which the conglomerates were formed. Because many of the sedimentary sequences are much thinner than elsewhere in Britain, a much greater span of geological time may be represented in a short distance on the ground. For example, 75 million years of the Carboniferous Period are represented in good exposures along one mile of the coast at Corrie; while a similar section on the Ayrshire coast extends for about 10 miles, and in Ayrshire the over-lying desert sands of the Permian are only exposed inland.

In addition to providing an introduction to a varied set of igneous and sedimentary rocks, Arran is also an excellent area for an introduction to the principles of geomorphology. Although the foundations of much of the scenery were developed during Tertiary times (the past 67 million years), this has been greatly modified by glacial events during the Pleistocene (the past 2 million years). Most of the glacial features in Arran are related to the last widespread (Devensian)

1

ice sheet which disappeared around 14,000 years ago; and the raised beach, which surrounds Arran and on which many of the coastal exposures occur, is probably related to isostatic rebounding since that time, about 14,000 years ago, and also following the Loch Lomond Readvance, which ended about 10,000 years ago. Thus much of the time-scale related to Arran geomorphology is in terms of thousands of years rather than millions.

It is these relatively recent events which are responsible for the shapes of the hills and valleys in Arran, and many of these processes are still continuing today. It is important for the geologist to observe modern erosion, transport and deposition of sediments so that comparison can be made with ancient equivalents. However, Arran lacks contemporary examples of other geological phenomena, such as active volcanoes, deserts and glaciers. We shall try to understand these phenomena solely by looking at the rocks in the field.

AIMS OF THIS GUIDE

Teachers often argue whether students should be taught about rocks in some depth before they are taken out into the field. The authors of this guide both came to Arran as undergraduates and we have subsequently taken many generations of students to the island. We are in no doubt that students can benefit enormously from a well-designed field course while still at school, or at a very early stage in their time at university or college. It is best to learn about the possible methods of emplacement of a dolerite or a granite while observing outcrops in the field, and it is an important part of geological education to compare modern sedimentary processes with the sedimentology of old formations. For example, modern rivers can be compared in many ways with the Old Red Sandstone rivers, and Arran is a suitable place to do this. Accordingly, we have written this guide assuming only a very basic geological knowledge on the part of the reader.

In the excursion itineraries, we often ask questions rather than give explanations. This reflects another important aspect of learning geology: the student should not be told what conclusions he is expected to draw. He needs to be shown what to look at, and guided to ask himself the right questions about what he sees. We aim to do both of these herein.

We assume that many readers of this guide will be in parties where the leaders are competent to discuss, confirm or deny students' interpretations and hypotheses. We have not supplied the answers to many questions which are asked in the excursions, though some answers may be found in Chapter 3, which should be read by all students beforehand.

BOOKS, MEMOIRS AND MAPS

Before starting work in the field the student should know something about the geology of Arran and its relationship to surrounding regions. In this guide, we give a brief summary of the geological development of the island, and a description of the 1:50,000 British Geological Survey (BGS) geological map of Arran (Solid edition). The BGS 1:250,000 (Clyde) sheet shows the solid geology on the sea floor around Arran; but perhaps the best beginning is for the student to examine carefully the BGS Ten Mile Map (1:625,000) North sheet, where the geology of Arran can be compared with the rocks of mainland Scotland and Northern Ireland.

For short, general descriptions of the rocks of Arran, the reader can consult the appropriate sections of 'Geology of Scotland' (Craig, 1983) and of 'Tertiary Volcanic Districts' (Richey, 1961), the latter in the BGS series of regional geology handbooks of Great Britain. Further details on the Dalradian rocks can be found in the 'Grampian Highlands' regional handbook (Johnstone, 1966). Other relevant handbooks in the same series are 'The Midland Valley of Scotland' (Cameron & Stephenson, 1985) and 'Northern Ireland' (Wilson, 1972).

The best summary of the geomorphology of Scotland is given by J. B. Sissons in 'Scotland' published by Methuen and Co. Ltd. (1976), in their series on the geomorphology of the British Isles. We have relied heavily on this book for parts of the guide. Arran is also mentioned in a more recent book on the environments present in Scotland during the past 30,000 years (Price, 1983). A further useful publication is the BGS 1:50,000 Drift edition geological map of Arran.

In addition to the regional geology handbooks, the BGS publishes detailed memoirs of the smaller areas covered by their 1-inch maps. The Arran Memoir, (Tyrrell, 1928) long unavailable, but now happily reprinted (1987), provides detailed factual information about the exposures, and is a mine of information for the specialist; but it is not recommended for the student.

Many scientific papers in specialist journals deal in part or entirely with Arran, and we have referred to some of these in Chapter 3 (Arran in Time and Space) and Chapter 4 (The Excursions) and listed them with other references at the end of this guide. Since Ramsay (1841) published his guide there have been many others. It is, however, with pleasure that we draw attention to 'Excursion to Arran' by J. W. Gregory and G. W. Tyrrell, and 'Isle of Arran' by S. I. Tomkeieff, produced by the Geologists' Association, respectively in 1924 in their Proceedings, and in 1961 to commemorate their Centenary. We have recommended to our own students for many years, 'Excursion Guide to the Geology of Arran' by Murray Macgregor (1965), with contributions from A. Herriot and B. C. King, and revised by J. G. MacDonald and A. Herriot (1983). This has many items of interest not covered here, including observations on the rich archaeology of the island, a topic which we omit entirely.

An interesting summary of the human history and economic development of the island is provided by Robert McLellan (1985).

CHAPTER 2

GEOLOGICAL MAPS OF ARRAN

THE REGIONAL SETTING OF ARRAN

Before starting a field course in Arran, it is useful to look at the island's position in relation to some of the major geological features of north-western Britain. McLean and Deegan (1978) provide a synthesis of the solid geology of the Firth of Clyde region, but the following discussion can be followed by referring to the BGS Ten Mile Map (scale; 1:625,000) North Sheet (1979) from which Fig.2 has been compiled.

The following points should be observed:

1. On the Ten Mile Map, the Highland Boundary Fault is clearly marked to the north-east of Arran, but Upper Palaeozoic rocks rest unconformably on the Dalradian in Kintyre and Antrim and there is no clear surface expression of this fault in Kintyre or Antrim to the south-west of Arran.

2. Compare Arran with the Tertiary igneous centres of Mull, Ardnamurchan, Rhum, and Skye. Which centres contain basalts, gabbros, granites, abundant sills? Which centres are associated with dyke swarms?

3. Note the stratigraphic sequence above the Permian in Antrim, and compare it with the Mesozoic and Tertiary blocks present in the Central Ring Complex (shown on the BGS 1:50,000 map).

4. Compare the widths of the outcrops of the Old Red Sandstone and Carboniferous rocks in Arran with those on the mainland in Ayrshire and Glasgow. Consultation of the Devonian (House *et al.*, 1977) and Carboniferous (George *et al.*, 1976; Ramsbottom *et al.*, 1978) correlation reports will show that the width of out-crop is roughly proportional to thickness, except in areas where the sequences are affected by gentle folding.

5. The outcrop of the Aberfoyle Slates (marked 21 on the BGS Map, 1979 edition, and shown also on Fig.2) occurs in a narrow belt just north of the Highland Boundary Fault, and continues into Arran. This belt marks the core of an inverted anticline. The beds to the north of this synform are greywackes of the Southern Highland Group on the inverted limb of the Tay Nappe (Shackleton, 1958, p.384); while the same greywackes to the south are steeply dipping to the south-east and are the right way up. The narrow outcrop of greywackes between the Aberfoyle Slates and the Highland Boundary Fault is partly due to the very steep dips, and partly because the beds are cut off by the Highland Boundary Fault.

4

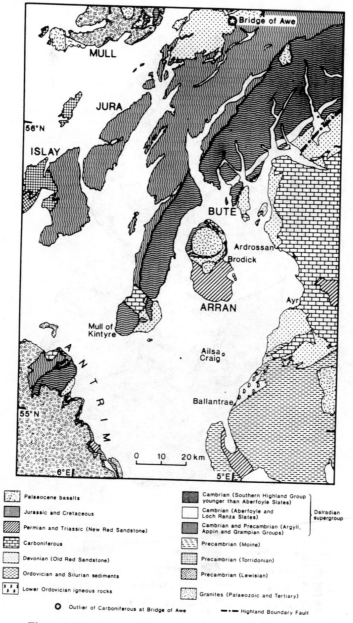

Figure 2: Outline geology of the region around Arran

W. S. McKERROW and F. B. ATKINS

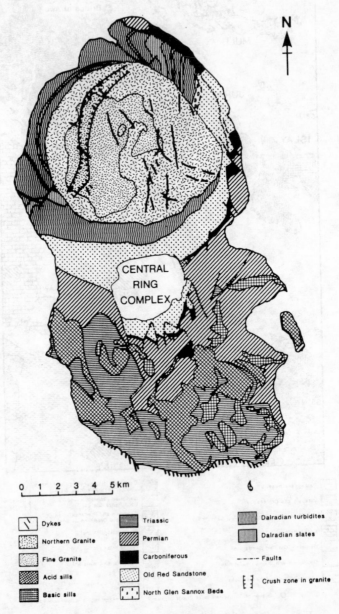

N

CENTRAL
RING
COMPLEX

0 1 2 3 4 5 km

	Dykes		Triassic		Dalradian turbidites
	Northern Granite		Permian		Dalradian slates
	Fine Granite		Carboniferous	----- Faults
	Acid sills		Old Red Sandstone		Crush zone in granite
	Basic sills		North Glen Sannox Beds		

Figure 3: Outline geology of Arran

6. There is a small outlier of Carboniferous sandstone and shales at Bridge of Awe (Johnstone, 1966, p.69) just to the north-east of the large area of Lower Old Red Sandstone lavas and sandstones of northern Argyll (Fig.2). While both the Upper Old Red Sandstone and New Red Sandstone conglomerates of Arran contain angular clasts and often much mica, which suggest derivation from nearby rocks, the Carboniferous sandstones are much more mature, and are probably derived by erosion of rocks well to the north of Bridge of Awe. The source area of the Lower Old Red Sandstone is more problematical (see pp.16–17).

7. The 1:250,000 Solid Geology map on the Clyde Sheet and the accompanying report (McLean & Deegan, 1978) shows the effects of post-Triassic faults in controlling some of the coastal features to the east of Arran. Remarkably there does not appear to be much indication of faulting to the north and west of Arran, where an elongate basin preserves some New Red Sandstone, which may be responsible for the red weathering and fissuring seen in places on the west coast of the island (Friend et al., 1970).

THE ARRAN MAP

Terminology and the map legend

On examining a geological map for the first time, it is essential to consider what the different colours indicate. On the BGS 'Ten Mile Map' (1:625,000), the sedimentary rocks are nearly all coloured according to their age rather than their rock type, while the metamorphic and igneous rocks are coloured on the basis of lithology. By contrast, the colours on the 1:50,000 map of Arran are based mainly on lithology.

In Arran, the exact age range of many sedimentary formations is unknown; for example, the top of the Stratheden Group is unlikely to correspond exactly to the end of the Devonian System. In this guide, we often describe the sediments using lithostratigraphic names (groups and formations) rather than the Period names. We also use the terms 'Old Red Sandstone' and 'New Red Sandstone'.

The BGS 1:50,000 geological map of Arran (and the simplified version in Fig.3) can be divided into three areas:

1. The Northern Granite and the surrounding Dalradian, Old Red Sandstone, Carboniferous and New Red Sandstone sediments.

2. The Central Ring Complex with its xenolithic blocks of Mesozoic sediments and Tertiary basalt, and the surrounding Upper Palaeozoic rocks.

3. The Permian and Triassic (New Red Sandstone) sediments of southern Arran with numerous sills and dykes.

1. Northern Arran

The large circular granite outcrop dominates the geological map almost as much as the granite peaks dominate the scenery in the field (Fig.4). Although the contact with the surrounding sediments is shown as a fault on the 1:50,000 map only in the extreme east (see also Tyrrell, 1928, Pl. III, p.158; Shackleton, 1958, p.377), it is very sharp, and the thermal aureole extends for more than 200m only in a few areas and is often much narrower (1:50,000 map and Tyrrell, 1928, p. 156-8). The evidence suggests that, at the time of final emplacement, the Northern Granite was nearly solid. Many of the faults to the east of the granite downthrow away from the intrusion and appear to be related to its emplacement (Woodcock & Underhill, 1987). The easterly plunge of the Sannox Bay anticline may also be related to uplift by the Northern Granite.

Around its northern end, the granite cuts across the strike of the slate bands in the Dalradian turbidite sequence and the strike appears to be continuous with the Dalradian of Bute, Cowal and other regions to the north-east of Arran (see Fig. 2 and BGS Ten Mile Map, North sheet, 3rd Edition (Solid) 1979). By contrast, the strike of the Dalradian rocks to the west of the Northern Granite has been bent parallel to the granite margin. We would concur with Tyrrell (1928, Pl. III, p. 158) in assuming that a major fault must be present along the contact in Glen Chalmadale and extending north-west to Loch Ranza to separate these two different areas of the Dalradian. However, it can also be seen from the 1:50,000 BGS map that the Catacol Synform, another structure related to the granite emplacement, is present in the Dalradian rocks on both sides of this postulated Loch Ranza Fault; the Loch Ranza Fault, therefore, is older than the intrusion of the Northern Granite.

The evidence from the 1:50,000 map alone is not sufficient to show that the anticline in the Dalradian to the north of the Northern Granite has been inverted. But Shackleton (1958) has demonstrated, by a study of the small-scale structures and their relation to way-up criteria like graded bedding, that this fold is the closure of a major fold. The lower, inverted limb of this fold extends westwards from the centre of the Loch Ranza Slates across to the Kintyre Peninsula, while the upper right way up limb is only exposed between the Loch Ranza Slates and the Highland Boundary Fault Zone to the south-east.

The geological map indicates a stratigraphic contact between the Dalradian and the North Glen Sannox lavas and Ordovician shales, but shows some Dalradian faulted to the east of the pillow lavas.

To the south of the Northern Granite, the contact between the Dalradian and the Lower Old Red Sandstone is now known to be an unconformity (Friend et al., 1963), although it is shown as a fault on older geological maps. The contact in North Glen Sannox is likely to be a fault as the Lower Old Red Sandstone is here brought in contact with both Dalradian and the North Glen Sannox lavas. This fault could be a continuation of the Highland Boundary Fault from Bute and the north-east, where the Lower Old Red Sandstone is known to be faulted against the Dalradian. At Corloch (NR 993490) the Stratheden Group rests directly on the Dalradian, and this area was thus uplifted prior to the Late Devonian, (to remove or to prevent deposition of the Lower Old Red Sandstone) i.e. it could lie north-west of the Highland Boundary Fault (Friend et al., 1963, p.390). Anderson (1947, p.504) considers that the two faults bounding the 'Upper Old Red Sandstone' at Corloch can be connected with faults in Bute, and that the eastern one of the pair is the Highland Boundary Fault. It is now thought that there may have been large strike slip (McKerrow, 1988a) or thrust (Bluck, 1985) movements on the Highland Boundary Fault prior to the Devonian; it is thus possible that

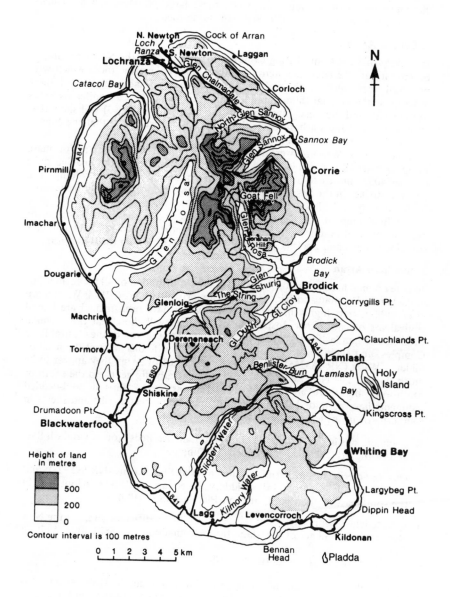

Figure 4: Outline physiography of Arran

the continuation of the fault, on which these large pre-Devonian movements" occurred, is now covered by Old Red Sandstone rocks.

2. Central Arran

It is likely that the Central Ring Complex is younger than the Northern Granite because it cuts the circular outcrops of the Upper Palaeozoic rocks which were previously deformed by the granite. One of the remarkable features of these outcrops is the gradual thinning and disappearance of the Carboniferous rocks to the south and the west. Inspection of the map (and its fig. 3) will show that each division of the Carboniferous thins towards the west; and that the change in thickness is thus not due to post-Carboniferous erosion.

After the Coal Measures were deposited, the Midland Valley saw a major phase of igneous activity (which in Arran is probably represented by the Imachar dyke (NR 863403)), but there is not much evidence of strong Hercynian folding. The dips and strikes in the basal New Red Sandstone differ only slightly from those in the underlying beds.

The BGS map of the Central Ring Complex shows the circular nature of agglomerate and granite outcrops, and how the north-east part of the complex contains many small pockets of hybrid mixture rocks within the outer granite.

3. Southern Arran

To date no map has been published showing the distribution of all the formations named in the Permian and Triassic Special Reports (Smith *et al.*, 1974; Warrington *et al.*, 1980). It is highly likely that many which have been named are lateral equivalents of each other. Inspection of the map will show that the Permian Brodick and Lamlash Beds have a narrow outcrop to the west of the Central Ring Complex, and again to the south-east of the Carboniferous inlier at the head of Sliddery Water (NR 985285), while on the east coast of Arran they appear to be much thicker. The New Red Sandstone beds generally dip gently to the south or south-west, but there are some local variations; gentle dips in well-bedded sediments have permitted the intrusion of numerous igneous sills and sheets in southern Arran, which can be classified as follows:

1. Crinanite sills in the Permian Brodick and Lamlash Beds around Lamlash Bay, and in the Triassic Auchenhew Beds at Dippin.

2. Quartz-dolerite sills in Permian sandstones at the Sheeans (NR 995328); and in Triassic siltsones around the Sliddery Water east of Blackwaterfoot, and in the south-east of the island; also on Pladda (NS 027190).

3. Quartz-feldspar-porphyry and felsite sills in many different levels in the New Red Sandstone all across the island from Drumadoon (NR 882288) to Whiting Bay.

4. The riebeckite-trachyte sill of Holy Island.

All the sills form prominent topographic features. Only the Holy Island sill is not cut by the dyke swarms. The dykes are best seen along the south coast of Arran. Stream sections suggest that they may be as numerous inland over much of the southern part of the island, but they are less abundant in the north.

CHAPTER 3

ARRAN IN TIME AND SPACE

INTRODUCTION

When we stand in Arran on Dalradian sediments originally deposited by turbidity currents in an ocean basin, it is natural to enquire about the nature and extent of this ancient basin, and what we can deduce about how the sediments were subsequently buried, folded and metamorphosed. When we examine rocks built of ancient desert sand dunes, we ask at which latitudes and under what climatic conditions these formed 250 million years ago. When we see the scores of dolerite dykes arranged in parallel formation along Arran's south coast, we wonder what larg-scale tectonic forces were stretching the crust to breaking point in Tertiary times.

Geologists have always asked questions such as these. The answers, in general, cannot be obtained by study of the Arran rocks alone. However, with the concepts of plate tectonics, sea-floor spreading and continental drift, we now have a much greater awareness of the way the Earth works as a whole, and in particular the way in which pieces of continental crust have been transported over the surface of the Earth, have collided, have grown, and have split apart.

This chapter attempts, therefore, to provide a broad, simplified framework in which the geology of Arran is seen against certain major global features and events such as the Palaeozoic Iapetus ocean, the closure of this former ocean with the collision of North America and northern Scotland with England and Europe, and the later separation (along a different line) to form the Atlantic.

Table 1 includes an indication of the changing latitudes of Arran through time; it is derived from estimates of continental positions by means of palaeomagnetism, facies and faunas (Bambach *et al.*, 1980; Scotese *et al.* 1979). In the Early Palaeozoic, Scotland was an integral part of the North American continent (with similar carbonate facies); in the Late Palaeozoic and Mesozoic, Scotland was still in low latitudes, but far removed from any continental margin until the opening of the North Atlantic in the Early Tertiary. There is still uncertainty about the Phanerozoic time-scale. That used in Table 1 is after Snelling (1985).

CAMBRIAN AND ORDOVICIAN

The oldest rocks in Arran are metamorphosed greywackes and shales belonging to the Southern Highland Group, the top division of the Dalradian Supergroup (Harris *et al.*, 1978) which outcrops over most of Scotland between the Highland Boundary Fault and the Great Glen Fault. The Southern Highland Group has yielded the Early Cambrian trilobite *Pagetides* near Callander in the Central

11

W. S. McKERROW and F. B. ATKINS

TABLE 1

SEQUENCE OF FORMATIONS, ENVIRONMENTS AND EVENTS IN ARRAN

AGE	FORMATION or ROCK	SEDIMENTS and ENVIRONMENTS *EVENTS*	LATITUDE
PRESENT		Peat, river and beach sediments, landslips	55.5°N
FLANDRIAN	Main Rock Platform	Beach deposits and caves	
10,000	(age doubtful; see text)	Moraines east of Goat Fell	
		Loch Lomond Readvance	
11,000			
		Lateglacial Interstadial	
14,000			
		Moraines, gravels, ice erosion	
		Last widespread ice sheet	
25,000			
		Short ice-free interval	
27,000			
		Main Devensian icesheet	
70,000			
IPSWICHIAN			
WOLSTONIAN		*Successive glacials and interglacials,*	
MIDDLE		Higher raised beaches and river	
PLEISTOCENE		terraces in Arran	
EARLY			
PLEISTOCENE			
2 Ma		*Elevation of Late Tertiary erosion level*	
PLIOCENE		Excavation of valleys	
		Uplift of Scotland	
5.5 Ma	Late Tertiary erosion level (peneplain) over Scotland		
MIOCENE			
24 Ma		*Palaeocene volcanics and the underlying rocks being*	55°N
		eroded through most of Tertiary time	
OLIGOCENE			
36.5 Ma			
EOCENE			
58 Ma	Dyke swarms	Crustal extension	54°N
	Sills of south Arran		
	Central Ring Complex	Collapse of volcanic caldera	
PALAEOCENE			
	Northern Granite	Intrusion with local uplift	
	Flood basalts	Terrestrial lava flows	
		Opening of North Atlantic Ocean	
66 Ma			51°N

CRETACEOUS	Chalk	Marine carbonates	
135 Ma	*No late Jurassic/Early Cretaceous deposits in Arran or Antrim*		43°N
JURASSIC	Lias	Marine clays and sands	
205 Ma			39°N
TRIASSIC	Westbury Formation (Rhaetian)	Black marine mudstones	
	Mercia Mudstone Group:		
	Dereneneach Formation	Grey-green siltstones	
250 Ma	Auchenhew Beds	Marine and lacustrine shales and sandstones	
	Break in deposition		32°N
PERMIAN	Lamlash Beds	Aeolian and fluvial sandstones	
	Brodick Beds	and conglomerates	
	Brodick Breccia	Fluvial conglomerates	
	Corrie Sandstone	Aeolian sandstones (the fluvial and aeolian Machrie sandstone may be equivalent)	
290 Ma	*Break in deposition, but Hercynian Orogeny not strong in Arran*		13°N
	Imachar quartz-dolerite dyke	E-W dykes in Midland Valley indicate N-S extension	
CARBONIFEROUS			8°N
	Coal Measures	Rivers and forests on deltas	
	Passage Group	Fluvial sandstones; volcanic ash	
	Upper Limestone Group	Deltaic sequences with limestones	
	Limestone Coal Group	Deltaic sequences with coals	
	Lower Limestone Group	Deltaic sequences with limestones	8°N
	Strathclyde Group	Sands and shales above basalt and mudstones	
	Inverclyde Group (inc. Kinnesswood Formation at base)	Sands and mudstones with cornstones	
362 Ma			
DEVONIAN	Stratheden Group (Upper Old Red Sandstone)	Fluvial conglomerates, sandstones and some cornstone-rich mudstones	
	The Acadian Orogeny (not strong in Arran)		
412 Ma	Lower Old Red Sandstone	Alluvial fans	
SILURIAN			0°N
435 Ma	*Folding of the North Glen Sannox Beds*		
ORDOVICIAN			15°N
	North Glen Sannox Beds	Deep marine basalts and shales	
510 Ma	*The Grampian Orogeny*		
CAMBRIAN	Southern Highland Group (Dalradian Supergroup)	Deep marine turbidites and shales	27°N

Region of Scotland, and the Middle Cambrian sponge *Protospongia* in western Ireland. The beds in Arran are thus likely to be of Early and Middle Cambrian age, though no fossils have been recorded here.

Most of the rocks were deposited as greywackes, and show graded bedding typical of turbidites, beds which have been laid down in submarine fans by turbidity currents. Some of the greywackes are coarse with small pebbles at the base of the graded layers, but others are thinner-bedded and fine-grained. Several thick mudstone and fine siltstone sequences occur within the greywacke succession; some of these may be fine-grained turbidites, but others show no sign of grading and appear entirely homogeneous except for rare discrete silt seams (which may be volcanic ashes in some instances). These fine-grained sequences may reflect long intervals of time between periods of turbidite deposition. The thick Loch Ranza Slates occur in the core of an anticline and are exposed in the old quarry (NR 963504) south of the path from Loch Ranza to Laggan Cottage (Excursion 3: Locality 1). The 1:50,000 BGS map shows two younger slate beds within the North Sannox Grits (Anderson, 1944, 1947). The younger of these slate beds is dark and rich in carbon; it reflects a time when anoxic conditions prevailed on the sea floor. It is best seen south of Catacol (NR 910486. Excursion 4; Locality 1).

The Grampian Orogeny occurred during the Early Ordovician (Tremadoc). In this orogeny, the Dalradian rocks of Arran were metamorphosed to chlorite grade in the greenschist facies (T less than 400°C, P less than 5 kilobars). They were folded and refolded, such that the anticline seen east of Lochranza is now inverted into a synform. This Aberfoyle Anticline can be traced many miles to the north-east across Scotland, just to the north of the Highland Boundary Fault; the beds to the north of this fold are all inverted and form the lower limb of the Loch Tay Nappe (Shackleton, 1958, pp.377, 384). Some later phases of this orogeny now appear to be post-Ordovician, occurring after the deposition of the North Glen Sannox Beds (see below), but with this exception, the rocks affected by the Grampian Orogeny are all confined to the region north of the Highland Boundary Fault.

The Dalradian rocks of Arran were again folded, much later, in Tertiary times, when the Northern Granite was intruded. One such Tertiary fold (clearly shown on the 1:50,000 BGS map around Loch Ranza) is the Catacol Synform (Fig. 8).

The development of cleavage is best seen in the (originally) more muddy Dalradian beds which have deformed more readily than the sandy beds. The slates contain abundant platy minerals, such as chlorite and muscovite; the orientation of these determines the cleavage. In simple fold structures, cleavage normally lies parallel to the axial planes of the folds, but in Arran this relationship is not always evident due to the complex nature of the fold history.

Another indication of the deformation which the Dalradian rocks have undergone, is the presence of numerous white quartz veins. The visitor to Arran will quickly realise that the distribution of these veins is not normally related to proximity to the Northern Granite nor to other igneous intrusions (though a few igneous veins are present in places). Instead, quartz veins are commonest in northern Arran and may be related to the area where folding of greywackes with a high original quartz content has been most intense (in the vicinity of the Aberfoyle Anticline and the Catacol Synform). Under certain circumstances (perhaps when quartz-rich sediments with a high water content are deformed) some of the quartz in the sediments is dissolved and reprecipitated in veins, which are generally roughly parallel to planes of weakness (bedding planes, joints or cleavage planes).

A sequence of shales and pillow lavas exposed in North Glen Sannox has long been considered to be possibly Ordovician, but only very recently have diagnostic fossils been found in them (Wheelan et al., in press). There is thus little doubt that the North Glen Sannox Beds are part of the Highland Border Group, which is seen in several small outcrops to the south of the Highland Boundary Fault on the Scottish mainland (Curry et al., 1984) These beds contain much fine-grained detritus which suggests that they cannot have been adjacent to the Grampian Highlands shortly after the Grampian Orogeny in the Tremadoc (Bluck, 1985). Johnson and Harris (1967) have demonstrated, however, that the North Glen Sannox Beds exhibit downward-facing structures: small folds which (together with the evidence from the pillows that the beds young to the east) suggest that the sequence lies on the eastward right-way-up limb of an overturned anticline. It may thus be that the North Glen Sannox Beds are related to the Aberfoyle Anticline in precisely the same way as the adjacent underlying Dalradian greywackes to the west. Some of the structures which are seen to affect Dalradian rocks close to the Highland Border would thus appear to be post-Ordovician (and pre-Devonian).

On the mainland of Scotland, the Highland Border Group is always separated from the Dalradian by the Highland Boundary Fault, although the Lower Old Red Sandstone is not (the Lower Old Red Sandstone rests unconformably on the Dalradian in both central Scotland and in Kintyre). It is possible that strike-slip movements of several hundred kilometres took place on the Highland Boundary Fault and the Southern Upland Fault before the Devonian (McKerrow, 1988a; Elders, 1987); and this would explain the apparent absence of Dalradian rocks below the Midland Valley (Upton et al., 1983; Conway et al., 1987). If these inferences are correct, it follows that the course of the Highland Boundary Fault in Arran can be only be located with reference to the pre-Devonian rocks, and that it lies between the Dalradian and the North Glen Sannox beds in north-east Arran, and to the south of all the Dalradian rocks exposed in central Arran.

SILURIAN

No Silurian sediments are known in Arran. During both the Ordovician and Silurian periods, the Scottish Highlands (including northern Arran) were uplifted as a result of the Grampian Orogeny and later events. By contrast, the Midland Valley was subsiding, as shown by inliers of Silurian sediments along the southern margin. It is possible that Silurian rocks are present at depth below the southern parts of Arran.

The Silurian and Early Devonian sediments of the Midland Valley were cut off from an ocean, which lay to the south of Scotland, by the rising mass of the Southern Uplands (Cocks et al., 1980). Strike slip (McKerrow, 1988a) or thrust (Bluck, 1985) movements persisted on the Southern Upland Fault until after the Wenlock, and it is clear that both margins of the Midland Valley are controlled by normal faults which follow the planes of weakness induced by these Early Palaeozoic structures.

DEVONIAN

After the docking of the Midland Valley with the Grampian Highlands in the Late Silurian (Bluck, 1985), the Highland Boundary Fault suffered repeated normal faulting. The main distinction between Highland scenery and the more subdued topography of the Midland Valley can probably be related to relatively late uplift (?in the Late Tertiary) along the Highland Boundary Fault. The greatest movements on the Highland Boundary Fault were of pre-Old Red Sandstone age, and in southern Arran the line of this fault may well be covered by Devonian and later sediments. During the Devonian, the Highland Boundary Fault zone marked a pivotal line (Bluck, 1969) separating areas of uplift and subsidence, though the line of the Highland Boundary Fault (along which major pre-Devonian movements occurred) is not necessarily related to the distribution of Lower Old Red Sandstone in south-west Scotland (Friend *et al.*, 1963), as Lower Old Red Sandstone lies unconformably on the Dalradian in Kintyre.

The Old Red Sandstone of the Midland Valley has been separated into Lower and Upper divisions; in common with many other areas adjacent to the Iapetus Ocean suture, these are separated by an unconformity which may mark the end of subduction (McKerrow, 1988b). However, in Arran the more diverse facies in the Old Red Sandstone (Friend *et al.*, 1963; BGS 1:50,000 map, fig. 2) tend to make this unconformity less obvious.

Plant fossils, assigned to *Psilophyton princeps var ornatus* Dawson (Tyrrell, 1928, p.31; Friend *et al.*, 1963, p.374) indicate an Early Devonian age for the Am Binnein Sandstones, the top formation in the Lower Old Red Sandstone south of Glen Rosa, where the basal breccia rests unconformably on the Dalradian (Excursion 1). The formations in the Lower Old Red Sandstone may have different ages in the sections exposed across the island (Friend *et al.*, 1963; BGS 1:50,000 map, fig. 2). The Old Red Sandstone (as now defined) is absent at Hutton's unconformity on the north coast of Arran. Renewed movements along the Highland Boundary Fault zone during the Devonian clearly controlled sedimentation (though the major Highland Boundary Fault plane bounding the southern margin of Dalradian rocks on which pre-Devonian movements were concentrated, must lie south of the Dalradian outcrops below the unconformity in Glen Rosa).

The clasts in the basal breccia of the Lower Old Red Sandstone (Garvock Group) in Glen Rosa are clearly derived from erosion of the local Dalradian rocks, and the Creag Mhor Conglomerate east of Dougarie contains clasts of andesite similar to the underlying Auchencar Lava (BGS 1:50,000 map, fig. 2). With these two exceptions, most Lower Old Red Sandstone clasts do not appear to have been derived locally. The larger clasts are predominantly of rounded pink quartzites, which, in the field provide the easiest means of recognizing the Lower Old Red Sandstone. Bluck (1984), Dickin (1984) and Haughton (1988) conclude that the Grampian Highlands did not contribute sediment to the Lower Old Red Sandstone of the northern parts of the Midland Valley, and as many current directions are from the south, a source within the Midland Valley seems probable.

The 'Upper Old Red Sandstone' of the Midland Valley has recently been assigned to new groups and formations (Table 1 and BGS 1:50,000 map) by Paterson & Hall (1986). Most of this sequence is assigned to the Stratheden Group, while the beds rich in cornstones at the top are now assigned to the

Kinnesswood Formation of the Inverclyde Group. This formation and also the upper parts of the Stratheden Group may well be of Early Carboniferous age.

In Arran, most of the Old Red Sandstone conglomerates are lenticular and cross-bedded. Some are followed by sets of cross-bedded sandstones and were deposited by alluvial fan streams (Bluck, 1967); other conglomerates are thicker, with erosional hollows, and are associated with both flat-bedded and cross-bedded sandstones suggesting braided stream deposits. In the Stratheden Group of Arran both the above types of conglomerates are present, but there are many more sand and silt sequences, typical of meandering rivers, where cornstones are present in the upper parts of these finer grained beds. The cornstones are calcareous nodules precipitated in sediments which were periodically dried out; such cornstones (or caliche) beds are usually situated on old flood plains or on other areas between river channels where intermittent flooding occurred. In the Stratheden Group, cornstones often occur in siltstones underlying coarse channel conglomerates at the base of the subsequent point bar cycle, but in the Kinnesswood Formation cornstone-bearing siltstones can occur without conglomerates.

On the west coast of Arran, the Stratheden Group consists of 375m of braided river deposits, while in the east, more sandstones are present and the sequence (870m thick) is mostly made up of point bar conglomerates and sandstones and overbank mudstones and siltstones with cornstones – deposits which are characteristic of meandering rivers. The conglomerates contain abundant angular clasts of vein quartz, schist (probably derived from the Dalradian close by) and red sandstone, in addition to the rounded quartzite (and subordinate lava) clasts so characteristic of the Lower Old Red Sandstone (Friend et al., 1963, p.394). The clasts suggest that some Lower Old Red Sandstone was being eroded as well as the Dalradian, and that the rivers were flowing from the west or the north.

On the north-east coast of Arran a thick sequence of cornstones in the Kinnesswood Formation (part of the Inverclyde Group) is present above the Stratheden Group. At Hutton's unconformity, north of Lochranza, the Kinnesswood Formation, with cornstones in overbank siltstones, is seen resting directly on the Dalradian. If any Old Red Sandstone was present in north Arran, it was removed before these sediments were deposited. Further south in Arran, the Lower Old Red Sandstone is thicker (1235m) in the west than in Glen Rosa (BGS 1:50,000 map, fig. 2), but the Stratheden Group is much thicker in the east. Clearly the relative rates of subsidence varied through time and from place to place.

The surface of the Dalradian rocks in north and west Arran is in many places stained red and contains fissures filled with sub-rounded Dalradian clasts. It has been suggested (Friend et al., 1970) that these features are related to a long period of weathering with little erosion, and that the unconformity above the Dalradian exposed near Newton (NR 936521) probably extends just offshore all along the coast to Dougarie in the west. Rocks of the Kinnesswood Formation occur above the unconformity near Newton, Carboniferous rocks form a shoal near Catacol, and the 1:250,000 map of the Clyde (Maclean and Deegan, 1978) shows submarine outcrops of New Red Sandstone along this stretch of coast.

All the Old Red Sandstone deposits in Arran were laid down in water. None of the sedimentary characters of the beds suggest an arid climate, though the presence of cornstones does point to a warmer climate in the later Devonian and in the Carboniferous where appreciable evaporation could take place between floods on the alluvial plains. World reconstructions suggest that Scotland was close to the Equator during the Devonian (Bambach *et al.,* 1980; Scotese *et al.,* 1979), and the sedimentary record is consistent with a position in the tropical rain-belt. The red colouration is due to a hematite coating on the sand grains. The small amount of iron in the sediments (3 to 5%) is in an oxidised state, and this reflects negligible amounts of organic material incorporated in the sediments. This may imply high sedimentation rates and high rates of erosion of the surrounding mountains; it may also reflect the fact that although the Silurian Period saw the first colonisation of the land by plants, even by Devonian times luxuriant forest growth was restricted to habitats not represented in Scotland.

CARBONIFEROUS

Although most of the Carboniferous sediments are clearly distinct from the Old Red Sandstone in both age and lithology, it has not been easy for the Geological Survey to draw a meaningful line on the map of Arran to separate the rocks of the two systems. The cornstone-bearing sandstones now assigned to the Inverclyde Group (Kinnesswood Formation) are taken as the base of the Carboniferous by the BGS (Paterson & Hall, 1986; BGS 1:50,000 map, 1987), but this arbitrary distinction, not surprisingly, has been disputed by several authors. Friend *et al.* (1963, p.372-3) and Tyrrell (1928, p.46-8) also considered that the 25m

TABLE 2

Classification of the Carboniferous rocks of the Midland Valley of Scotland (after George *et al.,* 1976; Paterson & Hall, 1986; BGS 1:50,000 map, 1987).

AGE	GROUP	
Westphalian C and D	Upper (Barren) Coal Measures	(absent in Arran)
Westphalian A and B	Productive Coal Measures	(no coals in Arran)
Namurian	Passage Group	(includes some volcanic rocks)
	Upper Limestone Group	(Index Limestone at base)
	Limestone Coal Group	(coal in Arran)
Dinantian	Lower Limestone Group	(Corrie Limestone at base)
	Strathclyde Group	(includes Clyde Plateau Volcanic Formation)
	Inverclyde Group	(Kinnesswood Formation at base)

of cornstones on the north-east coast (NS 003484) and the cornstones below the basalt at Corrie should be assigned to the Carboniferous, but Bailey (1926) and the BGS (1972 1:50,000 map of Arran) regarded them as part of the Old Red Sandstone. Before a discussion can take place on where exactly the Devonian-Carboniferous boundary lies, the formations making up the section need definition. The suggestion that the cornstones be assigned to the Kinnesswood Formation at the base of the Inverclyde Group (Paterson & Hall, 1986) helps to clarify the problem; but final solution awaits fossil discoveries. We can now assign all the beds between the Lower Old Red Sandstone and the Lower Limestone Group to the Stratheden, Inverclyde and Strathclyde Groups, and state that the Devonian-Carboniferous boundary probably occurs within the Stratheden Group.

Like the Old Red Sandstone, the Carboniferous sequences in Arran are generally much thinner than the equivalent successions on the mainland, and and range from 900 m. in the north-east to zero on the west coast at Machrie. This seems to be a reflection of smaller rates of subsidence; the sedimentary environments exhibited by the Carboniferous sediments in Arran appear to be generally similar to those in areas where much thicker sequences are present.

Inverclyde and Strathclyde Groups

In Arran these groups include the rocks deposited (or erupted) from the base of the Kinnesswood Formation to the base of the Corrie Limestone. The horizon of the Corrie Limestone can be traced over much of the Midland Valley (George *et al.*, 1976, p.48-9), and its fossils indicate a late Visean age. Prior to this, marine fossils are sparse and precise ages are uncertain.

In the western part of the Midland Valley, the thick development of the Clyde Plateau Volcanic Formation in the Strathclyde Group dominates the Early Carboniferous succession, so that the sequence includes relatively thin sediments above and below the lavas. Around Glasgow, many of the sediments in the underlying Inverclyde Group are lagoonal dolomitic limestones and shales, with some gypsum beds in places, while above the lavas, coastal, fluvial and deltaic sandstones and shales are present.

On the Laggan shore, 300m. of sediments are present in the Inverclyde Group above the Kinnesswood Formation (BGS 1:50,00 map, fig. 3), but elsewhere the cornstones of the Kinnesswood Formation are followed almost at once by the outpouring of basalt lavas at the base of the Strathclyde Group. At Corrie, the first signs of early Carboniferous igneous activity are sub-angular blocks of basalt set in a fine tuffaceous matrix. This poorly sorted 'agglomerate' is probably a mass flow deposit, where water-saturated igneous debris has moved down the slopes of a volcano. The succeeding basalt at Corrie is peculiar in that distinct flows are not seen. In much of the region around Glasgow, the top of each flow was weathered subaerially before the next flow erupted; this has led to the formation of 'trap topography' (trap is an old quarryman's name for basalt), stepped features resulting from the layers of alternating resistant (unweathered) and softer (weathered) basalt. From Arran, this trap topography can be seen looking east to the Little Cumbrae and the north Ayrshire hills above West Kilbride.

Lower Limestone Group

The Corrie Limestone, of late Dinantian age, occurs at the base of one of the many cyclothems, which are characteristic of the Carboniferous rocks above the Clyde Plateau Lavas. Rhythms of limestone, shale and sandstone with very variable thickness (5 to 80m) frequently show a coarsening-upward sequence from marine limestones, through shales and siltstones into sandstones. The sandstones are sometimes widespread and sometimes confined to a narrow channel when they may cut down into lower beds. Coals or rootlet beds in fine-grained sediments may be present above some sandstones. These cyclothems have been compared with modern deltas, and they represent progradations of a delta front (with distributary channels) over offshore marine deposits, and abandonment phases (Elliott, 1974), where muds deposited in lagoon or offshore environments may be followed by sandstones representing beaches or barrier islands.

Such rhythmic sequences may develop in a basin which is subsiding slowly and continuously, and be due entirely to delta switching, but changing sea levels (Ramsbottom, 1979) and tectonic movements have also been invoked to explain the Carboniferous cyclothems. It is probable that all three causes have been active in the British Carboniferous (Ramsbottom, 1981).

The western Midland Valley Carboniferous sandstones are all much richer in quartz than those in the Old Red Sandstone. Many have a small percentage of white mica, but feldspar is usually absent (Macgregor *et al.,* 1925, p.259). The quartz grains are cemented by quartz, calcite or mixtures of mica and kaolin. Some show indications of solution of the quartz grains at their points of contact (pressure solution); this would provide a source for the quartz cement. The carbonate cement could be derived by precipitation from water saturated in carbonates from one of the interbedded limestones.

Apart from the high proportion of quartz, the Carboniferous sandstones differ from those of the Old Red Sandstone in their white or yellow colour. They lack the hematite coating to the grains so characteristic of the Old Red Sandstone. These differences can be explained by consideration of the environments of deposition. The Old Red Sandstone was laid down by rivers within 20 or 30km of the region being eroded to supply the detritus. These distances were apparently not great enough to achieve the removal of many of the mica and feldspar grains, nor to remove the hematite coatings to the quartz grains. By contrast, the Carboniferous sandstones were deposited by coastal rivers, on beaches or on the fronts of deltas; that is, near the coast in low-lying regions just above or just below sea-level. By this time the areas under erosion extended far north of the Highland Boundary Fault zone. Outliers of Carboniferous occur north of the fault zone in Kintyre and north of the Clyde near Helensburgh; other outliers, much further north, occur beyond Mull, at Bridge of Awe (Fig. 2) and on the south-west of Islay (Johnstone, 1966, p.69). Although these Carboniferous deltas were bringing down much coarser material than, say, the modern Mississippi (which is 1,000km from the Appalachians and 2,000km from the Rockies) the sites of the deltas were perhaps at least 300 or 400km to the south of the source of the sediments. World reconstructions (Bambach *et al.,* 1980) suggest that Scotland was close to the equator in the Carboniferous and the facies present are consistent with a high rainfall and lush plant growth like many modern tropical regions.

Limestone Coal Group

Coals occur in post-Silurian deltaic sequences whenever very slow subsidence is present in non-marine environments. Such regions of non-marine subsidence were prevalent throughout the Midland Valley during the early Namurian (Ramsbottom *et al.*, 1978, p.32-3). Many important coal seams are present on the mainland, and the only coal in Arran occurs at this time, and was once worked on the Laggan shore. While marine limestones are absent (Francis, 1965, p.322) some marine shales occur, but the Midland Valley was generally more isolated from the sea during the deposition of the Limestone Coal Group.

Upper Limestone Group

In the late Namurian, marine limestones are again present in the deltaic sequences of the Midland Valley. In the Corrie section several thin fossiliferous limestones are present between Ferry Rock and the Corrie Hotel (Tyrrell, 1928, p.65). The lowest of these has been correlated with the Index Limestone, which is taken as the base of the Upper Limestone Group on the mainland. The limestones are interbedded with thick cross-bedded yellow sandstones, some mottled sandstones, and red and brown shales. While some of the red colour may be original, the colour of many of these beds may be related to oxidation below the New Red Sandstone. Bailey (1926, p.276) suggested that the ferric iron did not percolate downwards from the New Red Sandstone, but that it developed in place during the Permian through oxidation of ferrous iron above the water table. Bailey thus explained why some porous sandstones remain white or yellow: they are not red because they never had a large ferrous iron content (see also Mykura, 1960, p.74-5).

Passage Group

In the central parts of the Midland Valley, the latest Namurian beds are characterised by a sudden influx of coarse-grained fluvial sediments (Read, 1969). Equivalent beds in North Ayrshire and Kintyre contain some basalt flows overlain by the Ayrshire Bauxitic Clay (Francis, 1965, pp.329, 366-7).

In Arran, a bauxitic fireclay overlies a red ash in the Merkland Burn north-east of Brodick Castle and similar rocks are present in Benlister Burn south of the Central Ring Complex (Leitch, 1941). These are the only indications of the Passage Group in Arran. The Merkland Burn section shows an unconformity between the bauxitic fireclay and the lowest beds with Coal Measure bivalves, so perhaps the Passage Group is missing at Corrie and Laggan due to erosion prior to the Westphalian.

Coal Measures

In the Midland Valley, stratigraphic divisions of the Coal Measures can be recognised by means of goniatites, fresh-water bivalves and plants, but in Arran it is only the fresh-water bivalves and some rarer plant remains which indicate the age of these Upper Carboniferous beds. No Westphalian marine beds have been found. The bivalves indicate Westphalian A and B stages (Leitch, 1941). The youngest fossils are absent in the north of Arran (at Laggan and Corrie) suggesting a greater stratigraphic break below the New Red Sandstone in this area.

The Coal Measures in Arran also lack coals, though some seat-earths with rootlets mark the site where plants grew. Leitch (1941) noted that many of the sea-earths have an irregular upper surface and are followed by shales, occasionally with fresh-water bivalves similar to those forming the roofs of coal seams on the Scottish mainland. It appears that lack of sufficient subsidence to preserve coals may be the main reason for their absence in Arran; however, as Leitch states, 'the lithological sequence recalls that of normal Coal Measures sedimentation'.

Apart from the thinner sequences, another unusual feature of the Arran Coal Measures is the presence of many slumped sandstones and sandstone dykes. These are especially well developed on the Laggan shore near the Cock of Arran (NR 963517), and may be related to contemporary movements on the Laggan Fault (Leitch, 1941), which marks the contact beween the Carboniferous and the Dalradian in north-east Arran (Fig. 8).

At the end of the Carboniferous, the Midland Valley saw a major development of igneous activity, which included basic sills followed by an east-west dyke swarm. The only possible representative of this in Arran appears to be the quartz-dolerite Imachar Dyke (NR 864403), with a south-east/north-west trend which may reflect rotation during the intrusion of the Northern Granite.

The baryte veins in Glen Sannox cannot be directly dated, but most British baryte is known to be of Late Carboniferous age, and these veins in the Old Red Sandstone may well be the same (Dunham, 1952).

Although there was extensive igneous activity in the Midland Valley towards the end of the Carboniferous Period, the sequences in Arran show little angular discordance between the Coal Measures and the overlying Permian beds. Hercynian folding does not appear to be great, but the absence of the latest Carboniferous deposits in Arran suggests a long period of non-deposition between the equatorial high-rainfall deltas of the early Westphalian Coal Measures and the desert environments of the Permian.

PERMIAN AND TRIASSIC

The New Red Sandstone of Arran falls naturally into two groups which appear (as far as can be deduced given very limited fossil evidence) to correspond approximately to the two systems: Permian and Triassic. The lower group contains wind polished sand grains (present in both aeolian and waterlain sandstones), while the upper lacustrine and marine deposits are Triassic. All the Permian sandstones are red (the quartz grains being coated with hematite), while the Triassic sediments are very variable in colour. The Permian sediments of many parts of Britain indicate desert environments, and Arran probably lay between 15° and 30°N. during this period (Bambach et al., 1980; Scotese, et al., 1979). This is a latitude belt which contains many of the world's modern deserts.

In the headwaters of the Sliddery Water (NR 983283) a coarse sandstone with wind-polished grains is followed by lavas like those of the Mauchline Volcanic Group of Ayrshire (Leitch, 1941, p. 146-7) which are interbedded with deposits containing basal Permian plants (Smith et al., 1974, p.23). If the lavas are the same age in Ayrshire and Arran, then desert deposits developed in Arran very early in the Permian. Unfortunately, lack of detailed field mapping leaves us uncertain of the correlation of these Sliddery Water sections with the much better exposures on the shore sections where no basal lavas are present.

Lovell (1971, 1983) suggested that the basal New Red Sandstone at Machrie should be correlated with the Lamlash Sandstone because they both contain detrital agates (amygdale fillings of banded chalcedony) from Old Red Sandstone or Carboniferous lavas. Today wind blown sand can be seen to spread rapidly over large areas like the Sahara. We think that the incoming of wind polished sand grains (whether in the dune-bedded Corrie Sandstone or subsequently reworked in the river deposits of the Machrie Sandstone) is more likely to be synchronous than is the occurrence of detrital agates. The same reasoning would also suggest general correlation of the base of the Permian sequences in Arran and Ayrshire. In many deserts today, rare flash floods can rework wind blown deposits. These floods can be very local in extent, so it is not surprising that water deposited sediments are seen to occur at different levels within the different sequences over the island (Clemmensen & Abrahamsen, 1983).

Even the aeolian deposits like the Corrie Sandstone may have contained water close to the surface at times during the Permian. Fossil lightning strikes have been reported from Corrie and the Cock of Arran in dune-bedded sandstones (Harland & Hacker, 1966). Structures called fulgurites, consisting of a tube of fused sand with soft sediment in the middle are known to occur today where lightning hits soft sand. The examples from the Permian of Arran consist of tubes of colourless fused sand, with infills of red sand. This suggests (Harland & Hacker, 1966, p.669) that loose red-stained sand was present on the sand dunes and flowed into the fulgurites after they were formed. Unlike many modern desert sands these Permian sands appear to have been reddened before burial.

In the Permian (Smith et al., 1974) and Triassic (Warrington et al., 1980) Special Reports of the Geological Society of London, the system boundary is shown (with a great degree of uncertainty) to occur around the level of the Lamlash Sandstone. The only guides to age are the miospores which indicate an Early to Middle Triassic age for beds at Dippin (NS 049230); as these lie just above the highest beds with wind polished sand grains, it is possible that all the formations in Arran with wind polished sand grains are of Permian age. In Ulster, the desert environments are confined to the Lower Permian (Smith et al., 1974); if this were so in Arran, there may be a major stratigraphic break below the Triassic beds. The Triassic beds in Arran are now collectively assigned to the Auchenhew Beds (Craig, 1965, p.388; BGS 1:50,000 Map, 1987) and included in the Mercia Mudstone Group (Warrington et al., 1980) because of their general similarity to the Upper Triassic in England. The basal Auchenhew Beds (NR 885302) south of King's Cave on the west coast consist of parallel-bedded siltstones with halite pseudomorphs (mud casts of cubic salt crystals), some mudstones with desiccation cracks, and some fine sandstones with flaser bedding (wavy streaks of sand and mud), and have been interpreted as coastal mudflats and intertidal sandflats in a coastal area protected from the open sea (Pollard & Steel, 1978). Arthropod and worm burrows are also present (Pollard & Lovell, 1976; Pollard & Steel, 1978). The open sea appears to have lain to the south-west of Arran at this time.

The younger Triassic beds seen along the south coast of Arran and in the burn at Levencorroch (NS 011218) consist of parallel-bedded shales, siltstones and fine micaceous sandstones. Most of them are probably lacustrine, but no detailed sedimentology has been published. The presence of cornstones in some silts suggests high rates of evaporation in sediments exposed to the air.

The two youngest Triassic formations in Arran are only represented as xenolithic blocks in the Central Ring Complex. The grey-green siltstones of the Dereneneach Formation resemble the 'Tea-green Marls' of England (at the top of the Mercia Mudstone Group) and are thought to be of similar late Triassic age. Black mudstones, with a Rhaetian fauna, occur in the same (400 x 150m) block (Tyrrell, 1928, p.105-7); they are identical to the Westbury Formation of England (Warrington et al., 1980, p.26) and indicate the wide extent of the Rhaetian marine transgression. Some earlier Triassic beds also occur as blocks which fell into the caldera of the Central Ring Complex volcano; the red and green siltstones on Windmill Hill (NR 983351) are probably referable to the Auchenhew Beds.

JURASSIC AND CRETACEOUS

The Central Ring Complex represents the caldera of a Tertiary volcanic centre, into which blocks of the associated sediments subsided. These include fragments of Old Red Sandstone (often just isolated pebbles derived from conglomerates, but now in an igneous matrix) and much larger blocks of Permian (?), Triassic, Lower Jurassic, Upper Cretaceous sediments and Tertiary basalts (Tyrrell, 1928; King, 1955). The blocks present are precisely those formations seen in Northern Ireland along the Antrim coast, and it would appear that each formation once extended over Arran. The absence today of this succession above the Central Ring Complex gives some indication of the amount of erosion over Arran during the Tertiary. The average thicknesses in Ireland (Wilson, 1972) are comparable with King's (1955) estimate of the pre-caldera stratigraphic succession in Arran (Table 3).

TABLE 3

	Northern Ireland (metres)	Arran (metres)
Tertiary basalts	550	>100
Cretaceous chalk and sandstone	140	20?
Lower Lias	100-300	15?
Rhaetian mudstones	15	30?
Triassic (Auchenhew Beds)	75-1,100	300
Permian (Lamlash and Brodick Beds)	100-200	600
TOTAL	1,650-2,300	>1060

It appears that between 1000m and 2000m of rocks were removed from Arran by erosion, after the extrusion of early Tertiary basalts. Some of the blocks must have descended this distance into the collapsed caldera of the Central Ring Complex.

Fortunately, fossils have been preserved in many of these blocks. The Lower Lias sandy shale on Windmill Hill (NR 983351) has yielded smooth, evolute ammonites now identified (Warrington *et al.*, 1980, p.26) as probably Sinemurian (the second stage of the Jurassic). After the Lias, no sediments are known in Antrim until the Late Cretaceous, and again the same interval is missing in the Central Ring Complex blocks: the only post-Lias blocks are of sandstone, chalk and basalt.

TERTIARY

Igneous activity

The Atlantic Ocean began to open between West Africa and the United States about 200 million years ago (Dietz & Holden, 1970), but subsequent rifting further north has occurred at different times in different places. One major, if short-lived, series of events is associated with rifting west of the British Isles. In north-eastern Ireland and parts of western Scotland, high rates of heat flow in the mantle, combined with tensional forces in the overlying continental crust, gave rise to widespread and diverse igneous activity for a short period in the Lower Tertiary.

This area, extending from Carlingford, Ireland in the south to Skye and St. Kilda in the north and north-west, is known as the British Tertiary Province. For a hundred years it has provided a major focus for research in igneous petrology, and has been an invaluable training ground for generations of geologists.

In the British Tertiary Province as a whole, activity may have commenced as early as 65 million years ago, and continued until 54 million years ago, but there are uncertainties in some of the published dates, and the entire episode may have been confined to a period of only one or two million years (Macintyre *et al.*, 1975). Activity occurred in three main stages.

a) Early flood basalts. Feeder dykes and fissure eruptions gave rise to voluminous quantities of plateau basalt lavas.

b) High level plutonic centres and central volcanoes, ring complexes, cone sheets and calderas involving both basic and acid magmas.

c) Dyke swarms, chiefly of basic rocks.

An excellent modern review of the British Tertiary Province is provided by Sutherland (1982).

Arran is located approximately at the centre of the province, and provides examples of many of these phenomena. Tertiary igneous rocks comprise nearly 50% of the surface area of the island, if superficial drift deposits are ignored. A recent assessment of ages for the Arran rocks (Dickin *et al.*, 1981) suggests that, with the exception of the early flood basalts of which only fragments are preserved, activity lasted for no more than one million years. Indeed, the dates are so tightly bunched around 59 Ma. that relative ages must be deduced from field and structural relationships (Table 4).

TABLE 4

A provisional chronology for the Tertiary igneous rocks

(Ailsa Craig plug	riebeckite granite) ⎱	
Holy Island sill	riebeckite trachyte ⎰	58.5 Ma (a)
Acid sills and dykes	felsites	
Acid sills and dykes	quartz feldspar porphyries	58.5 ± 1.6 Ma(b)
Basic sills		
(oversaturated)	quartz dolerites	
Basic sills and cone		
sheets		
(undersaturated)	crinanites	

Central Ring Complex

Volcanoes within resurgent caldera ⎱	granites, gabbros,	58.3 ± 4.4 Ma (c)
	intermediate hybrids,	
Caldera collapse	felsites, andesites,	
	basalts, pyroclastics,	
Central volcano ⎰	foundered xenoliths	

Northern Granite

	aplites and pitchstones	
Inner granite pluton	fine-grained granite	
Outer granite pluton	coarse-grained granite	⎰ 58.8 ± 1.2 Ma (d)
		⎱ 60.3 ± 1.6 Ma (e)

Fissure eruptions	plateau basalt lavas	?63-60 Ma (f)

Basic dykes were intruded throughout most of the period of igneous activity except the latest.

(a) Deduced from K/Ar & Rb/Sr data (Macintyre *et al.*, 1975)
(b) K/Ar age (Mussett *et al.*, 1987)
(c) K/Ar age (Evans *et al.*, 1973)
(d) K/Ar age (Evans *et al.*, 1973)
(e) Rb/Sr age (Dickin *et al.*, 1981)
(f) By analogy with Skye, Mull and Antrim (Pankhurst, 1982)

Plateau basalts

The Tertiary igneous succession began with the outpouring of basaltic lavas from fissure eruptions. By analogy with the extensive tracts of *in situ* flood basalts in Skye and Mull, it seems likely that similar flows may have covered much or all of Arran. However, remnants of these lavas are now found only in the Central Ring Complex. Here giant xenolithic blocks overlying Cretaceous sediments, including one up to 1.5 km in length, owe their preservation to caldera collapse of the complex, when pre-existing rocks subsided some 1000 m (King, 1955). These lavas, although now more or less altered, are olivine-bearing, and show affinities with the early plateau-type basalts in other parts of the Province. Elsewhere on the island, post-Tertiary erosion has obliterated all traces of Late Mesozoic sediments and Early Tertiary volcanic rocks.

It is not possible to identify feeder dykes for the early basalts with any degree of confidence. Of the many hundreds of dykes which do not cut younger Tertiary intrusions, those of appropriate composition constitute possible candidates, especially if they have well-developed thermal aureoles, implying a prolonged period of magma movement within a fissure.

The Northern Granite

The scenery of Arran is dominated by the rugged, glacially-sculpted granite mountains that rise to 874 m (Goat Fell) in the north of the island. These are built of the Northern Granite, a pluton having a nearly circular outcrop area of 146 km^2 and forming the most conspicuous feature on the 1:50,000 geological map.

The pluton consists of two members, an earlier, outer, coarse-grained granite, and a younger, inner, fine-grained granite. Petrographically both consist of quartz, orthoclase, albite-oligoclase, perthite, and biotite, with accessory titanomagnetite and sphene. Small differences in trace element chemistry indicate that the fine-grained granite is the more highly fractionated (Johnston & Meighan, 1975). Unlike other granites in the province, the Northern Granite of Arran lacks secondary hydrous minerals such as epidote, although the mineral is present in the metamorphic aureole. The outer granite is somewhat porphyritic in places. Both granites contain miarolitic cavities carrying euhedral crystals of feldspar and quartz, the latter sometimes smoky or coloured; and rarely of beryl, topaz, garnet and stilbite. Dark, partly digested xenoliths of fine-grained basic rock and/or country rock sediments are sparsely distributed.

At present erosional levels the intrusion generally has a steeply dipping, often vertical outer margin. The surrounding country rocks consist of Dalradian greywackes except in the east where the contact is partly faulted against Devonian sediments; they have been forcibly updomed and faulted by the granite. The Catacol synform in the Dalradian to the north is also an expression of this forcible updoming.

The contact between the inner and outer granites is generally sharp (Flett, 1942), and the latter is older. The form of the inner granite is not known; it may be stock-like in three dimensions, although the highly irregular outcrop pattern to the east is not easy to explain (Emeleus, 1982).

For an intrusion of this size, the outer margin is somewhat unusual in several respects. First, there is very little evidence of chilling of the granite against the country rocks. In places grain-size decreases gradually outwards over a zone of up to a metre in width, but more often this zone is only a few centimetres or less in width. Second, there is a notable absence in general of veins or stringers of late-stage siliceous residua forming apophyses in the country rocks. Third, there are no pegmatites and no mineralisation of the kind associated with, say, the Cornish granites.

Both inner and outer granites have been subjected to post-consolidation movements represented by zones of dynamic crush-brecciation. These are usually only a few centimetres wide, although Tyrrell (1928) drew attention to a major zone of crushing some 1 km in width and 14 km in length crossing both granites transgressively in the west (Fig.3). These crush zones may be related to later Tertiary movements along the zone of the Highland Boundary Fault (Emeleus, 1982), although we prefer to ascribe them to late-stage movements of the pluton after it had largely consolidated. Many of the other observable features of the Northern Granite, described above, are consistent with this concept. In brief, a mass of granitic magma rose diapirically in the crust, and more rapid heat losses at the top of the column led to crystallization before upward movement had entirely ceased. The upper parts of the pluton, those now exposed, would thus have been largely crystalline when finally emplaced; liable to localised fracturing (the crush zones); too cool to produce a wide thermal aureole, or form a sizeable chilled margin; too 'dry' to vein the country rocks; and sufficiently competent to dome the country rocks and form the faulted, mylonitised junction to the east.

The margin in the north-west, near Catacol (Excursion 4) is, in several respects, atypical. Here the highly irregular contact, veining of the country rock, and stoped Dalradian xenoliths all indicate that locally the granite was still at, or close to, liquidus temperatures at the time of emplacement.

On the basis of previously known features, described above, but especially in the light of an analysis of fault systems in the New Red Sandstone, Woodcock and Underhill (1987) have recently proposed an emplacement model for the Northern Granite that involves two-stage 'ballooning'. Early inflation of a hemispherical pluton produced radial stretching of the overlying cover, followed by strong concentric dip-slip displacement over its flanks. Older faults in the sub-Permian basement were reactivated and the strain propagated upwards as zones of micro-faulting in the poorly consolidated desert sandstones of the Permian (See Excursion 6, Locality 18). The later intrusion of the inner fine-grained granite caused radial expansion, accommodated chiefly by strike-slip movement on major conjugate faults in the south-east.

The final event in the cooling history of the pluton was the injection within the granite of thin veins of aplite, a type of fine-grained microgranite representing residual liquids relatively poor in volatile constituents. It may be significant that the aplites tend to be more abundant within the crush zones. Except in these zones, aplites are not especially conspicuous in the granite mountains, although curiously most of the larger granite erratics along the shore seem to contain an aplite vein!

The Central Ring Complex

The oval-shaped region of igneous rocks averaging 5 km in width to the south of the Northern Granite (Fig.3) was aptly named by Tyrrell (1928). Not only is it located near the island's geographical centre, but it is formed from the exposed roots or 'hearth' of a volcano (later a cluster of volcanoes) that was *central* in the geological sense. The term *'ring'* refers to the annular outcrop patterns formed by the granite and agglomerates comprising the outer parts of the region (see 1:50,000 geological map). The region is *complex* in several ways. Many intrusive and extrusive igneous rock types are represented, and poor exposures hinder map-making and the interpretation of interrelationships. Insofar as the history of the centre has been unravelled, chiefly by Gunn (1903) and King (1955), it is apparent that later events to a large extent have obliterated or obscured early events.

The Central Ring Complex, like the Northern Granite, has caused some doming of the surrounding sediments; its outer margins to the east and west are largely fault-bounded. Careful study of the 1:50,000 map reveals that the complex cuts the structure imposed by the Northern Granite, and it may thus be deduced that the focus of activity has with time shifted from the north to the centre of the island.

The igneous rock types of the complex include dacites, andesites and rhyolites forming *in situ* lava flows; acid pyroclastic agglomerates, granites and micro-granites; and a variety of hybrid rocks of gabbroic and dioritic bulk compositions, formed by the assimilation of pre-existing coarse-grained mafic rocks by acid magmas (Harker, in Tyrrell, 1928). Of these rock types, far and away the most abundant are the granites and acid agglomerates. These have crudely circular concentric outcrop patterns; they may be ring-dykes having a similar origin to the well-studied examples in Mull, Ardnamurchan and Skye (Bell, 1982). They formed late in the history of the Central Ring Complex (King, 1955).

King (1955) has proposed a tectonic history for the Complex that begins with updoming, followed by subsidence of up to 1000 m to produce a caldera in which individual volcanic centres finally developed.

One of the more interesting aspects of the complex, (and which can be demonstrated in the course of a short field excursion!), is the occurrence within the caldera of large xenolithic blocks of late Mesozoic and early Tertiary rocks. These blocks consist variously of Old Red Sandstone, New Red Sandstone, Rhaetian, Liassic and Cretaceous sediments, and Early Tertiary plateau lavas. All were probably in their time deposited throughout Arran, but those of Rhaetian age and younger have since been entirely eroded away beyond the confines of the caldera.

Sheets and sills of central and southern Arran

Numerous igneous sheets and sills of a variety of compositions dominate the geology (and largely determine the topography) of the southern half of the island. These hypabyssal rocks intrude Permian and Triassic sediments. Although a detailed chronology for these rocks remains uncertain (Table 4), they all appear in general to post-date the rocks of the Central Ring Complex, implying another southwards shift in the focus of activity. It may be noted that this southwards migration of activity in Arran contrasts with an alleged northwards migration in the province as a whole, interpreted by Duncan *et al.* (1972) as evidence for movement of the European lithospheric plate progressively southwards over a stationary mantle plume in Palaeocene times.

The larger sills of southern Arran may be divided petrologically into three groups:-

a) The crinanites. These are analcite-bearing olivine dolerites, forming the Claughlands, Monamore Glen and Kingscross sills, respectively to the north, west and south of Lamlash; and the Dippin sill in the south-east corner of the island. Tomkeieff (1961) has suggested that the Lamlash group is connected at depth and represents a cone-sheet complex. Study of drill-core samples from the Dippin sill (Gibb & Henderson, 1978) has revealed a history of multiple intrusion, combined with fractionation before, during and after episodes of emplacement. These complexities cannot, unfortunately, be demonstrated in the field. Analcite, a major constituent of the large basic alkaline intrusions of Arran, has replaced primary nepheline (Henderson & Gibb, 1977).

b) The quartz dolerites. These sills form conspicuous features in the south-east of the island, notably Auchenhew and Levencorroch Hills, the waterfalls in Glen Ashdale, and the small island of Pladda to the south. Dykes of the same composition are relatively rare.

c) Acid sills. These include quartz-feldspar porphyries, e.g. Bennan Head, Drumadoon and Brown Head; pitchstones, e.g. Corrygills pitchstone; and felsites, e.g. Torr Righ Mor, Beinn Tarsuinn and Innis Dubh.

The relative ages of the minor sheet and sill intrusions in central and southern Arran are not known in detail, although Tyrrell (1928) has suggested certain time relationships, deduced from field evidence (see also MacDonald & Herriot, 1983, pp.46-49).

Composite sills and dykes

Although some of the major sills have margins of contrasting composition, the series of dykes and sills along the shore between Tormore and Blackwaterfoot in the west, known collectively as Judd's dykes (Judd, 1893), provide classic examples of composite intrusions. These are described in some detail later (Excursion 4). Recent isotopic and geochemical studies (Dickin *et al.*, 1981) indicate that the composite intrusions reflect the simultaneous availability of acid and basic magmas, these both being differentiates of mantle melts affected by variable amounts of contamination within the crust. A modern overview of the interesting problems posed by the composite intrusions of the British Tertiary Province is provided by King (1982).

The basic dykes

The BGS 1:50,000 geological map (solid edition) depicts the basic dykes in shades of green, and many have now been subdivided on the basis of their chemistry and petrography (e.g. olivine-dolerite, olivine-tholeiite, tholeiite, crinanite, etc.); the few quartz dolerite dykes are shown in blue. Perusal of the map leads to the following generalizations.

a) The great number of dykes exposed along the south coast. More than 230 occur between Dippin Head and Bennan Head, a distance of about 7km, representing a percentage dilation of 7%, locally increasing to 12%.

b) Lesser concentrations elsewhere. Along the east, west and north coasts, exposures are good, so that the map depicts a real difference. Inland the relative paucity of dykes is more apparent than real since large numbers are undoubtedly hidden beneath drift deposits.

c) A crude sub-radiate pattern in the central and northern parts of the island, suggesting a relationship here between some of the dykes and the major intrusive centres.

In the older literature, most of the basic dykes were assigned to the great regional dyke swarms of the British Tertiary Province, and ascribed to a late stage in the igneous history of the region. Recent studies, however, have begun to reveal a finer structure (Speight, *et al.,* 1982), and there seems little doubt that dyke formation occurred throughout the period of time with which we are concerned. Subswarms associated with the main intrusive centres probably account for many of the sub-radiate dykes in the central and nothern parts of the island. Many along the south coast with a NNW-SSE trend appear to conform to the main regional swarms, but even here ten episodes of dyke formation have been recognised on the basis of changing orientation and magma compositions with time (Halsall, 1978).

The last event in the Tertiary igneous history of Arran may have been the intrusion of the thick sill-like mass of riebeckite-trachyte forming Holy Island to the east. The riebeckite-granite plug forming the island of Ailsa Craig 20km to the south of Arran, may also represent a late event.

Origin of the magmas

Although it is widely accepted that the basic igneous rocks of the British Tertiary Province are essentially the products of partial melting in the mantle, the origin of the acid magmas has been the subject of a considerable research effort, the chief question being the extent to which these are mantle-derived differentiates or the products of crustal melting (anatexis). Thompson (1982) provides a modern review of this subject. The latest isotopic and geochemical work on the Arran rocks (Dickin *et al.,* 1981) supports the differentiation hypothesis for this part of the province, although the acid magmas thus produced have suffered varying amounts of subsequent contamination within the crust. A fuller discussion of these matters lies outside the scope of this guide.

Geomorphological Development

Since the extrusion of the Tertiary basalts (60 million years ago), between 1,000 and 2,000m of cover has been eroded from above the Central Ring Complex. Much of this removal probably took place shortly after the uplift associated with the igneous activity, when erosion rates would have been greatest, but even so the erosion base levels would have been well above the present mountain tops for the greater part of the Tertiary (Sissons, 1976, p.34; George, 1966).

We now know (Chesher *et al.*, 1972) that younger (and softer) rocks occur offshore around much of Scotland. The form of the present coastline is, in many places, the result of removal by the sea of weak down-faulted cover rocks from above the underlying, older, resistant rocks (Sissons, 1976, p.36). George (1966) ascribed most high-level surfaces to marine erosion, but Sissons (1976) concluded that marine erosion surfaces only ever existed at low altitudes, and that the peaks of the Northern Granite mountains (from 700 to 874m) are remnants of a sub-aerial erosion surface which developed during the mid-Tertiary.

At less than half the height of the highest peaks in northern Arran, there is a marked platform (mostly on Dalradian and Old Red Sandstone outcrops) around the Northern Granite at about 300 to 400m (Creag Ghlas Laggan NR 973503; Maol Donn NS 019406; Glenshant Hill NR 990396). This is a late Tertiary erosion level, above which the granite peaks would have stood up as monadnocks. In the older literature (Tyrrell, 1928, p.257) this platform was considered to be Pliocene in age; this may well be so, but there is no evidence for its precise age. The platform appears to decrease in level from 500m on the hills of the Central Ring Complex to 270m on Auchenhew Hill (NS 015227) on the south coast. These changes in altitude could be due in part to an original south-sloping gradient, and in part to subsequent warping or faulting.

The last major geomorphological event before the Pleistocene (Table 1) was the uplift of this Late Tertiary platform, perhaps from just above sea level to near its present height. This event can be deduced from the presence of deep, narrow valleys (like Glen Rosa and Glen Iorsa) in all the upland areas of Scotland (Sissons, 1976, p.36). If this uplift had occurred very long before the Pleistocene, it could be inferred that these upland valleys would now be much wider, and the landscape more mature, but there is no direct evidence to suggest exactly when this late uplift took place.

Some upland valleys may have existed before this late Pleistocene uplift, but the general form in which we now see them probably dates from this time. In the Northern Granite, the valleys often followed dykes, faults, or other lines of weakness. It is possible that some of the main through valleys, like the String in Arran, may be older than the rest (Gregory, 1920; Tyrrell, 1928, p.256-9).

PLEISTOCENE

History

From the evidence in many parts of the world, it is seen that many Mediterranean and Boreal climates became cooler about 2 million years ago. Until the early 1970's this change was taken to mark the start of the Pleistocene (Mitchell *et al.*, 1973, p.3), but in recent years pollen stages have been correlated with magnetic reversals and the base has been redefined such that several British deposits previously regarded as Lower Pleistocene are now thought to be Pliocene (Curry *et al.*, 1978, p.55). However, the precise boundary is of no great relevance in Scotland. In contrast to the marine sequences of East Anglia and the river and lake deposits of the English Midlands, there are no records of Lower Pleistocene deposits in Scotland; some peat in Shetland and some shelly boulder clay in Buchan may be as much as a million years old (Mitchell et al., 1973, pp. 54, 59), but the great bulk of Scottish Pleistocene deposits and erosion features are much younger (Table 1).

The last stage of the Upper Pleistocene, the Devensian, marks a cooling of the climate at about 70,000 B.P. (years before present) which followed a long interval of more temperate climates (Mitchell, 1981, pp.241, 246-7). Some boulder clay in Kintyre may be of Early Devensian age (Mitchell et al., 1973, p.54). Glacial conditions in Scotland may have continued (perhaps with some warmer interludes) from 70,000 B.P. until about 27,000 B.P., after which Scotland may have had no permanent ice cover for 2,000 years (Sissons, 1976, p.84).

The ice advance which left the most obvious features over the whole of Scotland perhaps started about 25,000 B.P. and reached its peak between 18,000 and 17,000 B.P. (Sissons, 1976, p.84). This was followed by a warmer interlude at around 13,000 B.P.; beetles from a site near Lockerbie indicate a climate not much colder than that prevailing today (Sissons, 1976, p.90); and by 12,500 B.P. all the ice may have receded from Scotland (Sissons, 1976, p.93).

The climate did not remain mild for long. By 10,800 B.P., ice fields had started to accumulate again in the Western Highlands to the north of Loch Lomond. This Loch Lomond Readvance reached its peak at 10,500 B.P., by which time the Northern Granite peaks of Arran were again glaciated (Sissons, 1976, pp.92-3, 106), but the Arran ice cap was isolated from the main field, which extended from Loch Lomond to Skye, and which appears to coincide with an area that still has high rainfall today. There is some debate about which features in Arran may correspond to the Loch Lomond Readvance, but Sissons (1976, p. 102) considers that only the moraines studded with boulders on the eastern flanks of the Goat Fell ridge are related to this readvance. All the other glacial features in Arran are probably related to earlier ice, and in particular to the last widespread ice sheet, which reached its peak around 17,500 B.P. and perhaps did not all go until about 13,000 B.P. The main lateglacial shoreline probably developed near the start of the Loch Lomond Readvance (Sissons, 1981; Jardine, 1982); at this time sea level around Arran was only 2 to 4m above the present level.

Many of the erosional features of Arran, like the U-shaped valleys and the corries, were perhaps developed progressively during cold spells throughout the Pleistocene, but of the depositional features related to ice (moraines, eskers, drumlins, outwash gravels and erratic blocks) only those related to the last ice sheet are commonly preserved. Some interglacial clays occur in southern Arran (Tyrrell, 1928, p.263) with a marine fauna containing several species which today extend from Scotland to northern Scandinavia.

Erosional features

The Northern Granite peaks were high enough to form a centre of ice accumulation separate from the rest of the Scottish Highlands (Sissons, 1976, p.37). The movement of ice away from this region resulted in the development of U-shaped valleys. The glaciers not only changed the shape of the valleys, but gouged out the valley floors. Hanging valleys in Glen Iorsa and Glen Rosa indicate overdeepening by ice of 150 to 250m (Sissons, 1976, p.41).

The peaks of the Northern Granite show two distinct types of shape. Goat Fell, Cir Mhor and other peaks to the east of Glen Iorsa over 750m high, all have rugged summits with many steep and angular rock faces. By contrast, the western hills (the highest is Beinn Bharrain, 721m) have rounded profiles; the only rugged terrain in the west is well below the summit level, around corries and on the sides of glacially deepened valleys. It would appear that, at some stage, the ice sheet covered the summits of the lower hills in the west, while the higher eastern peaks stood out through the ice as nunataks (the late J. V. Harrison, personal communication, 1955; see also Gregory, 1920, p. 151).

At later stages of glaciations, when the level of the ice cap was much lower, corries developed on some of the Northern Granite slopes. Today, the floors of most of these corries are between 350 and 400m above sea level, and, with a few exceptions, they lie on the north or east sides of the peaks (away from the sun?).

Depositional features

Much of the southern half of Arran is covered by boulder clay (BGS 1:50,000 Drift map of Arran), usually in no very distinctive form, but between Dougarie and Machrie some drumlins are present (Tyrrell, 1928, p.260). Some of the mounds in this area are deposits which accumulated on the down-flow side of a crag, and can be termed 'crag and tail'. Other smaller crags, like those on the slopes of Cnocan Donn (NR 906246), are roches moutonées with smooth northern faces and rugged, steep southern faces, where the southward moving ice has plucked away the rock on the down-flow side.

In the Northern Granite valleys and in the northern parts of the Central Ring Complex, the last retreat of the valley glaciers is marked by terminal moraines. Some lateral moraines are also present in places (Tyrrell, 1928, p.263-4). In Glen Dubh, a terminal moraine (NR 992340) once dammed the upper part of the glen to form a small loch. Eventually the moraine was breached, but the flat bottom of the former lake is easily distinguished. There is also in Glen Dubh a line of hillocks parallel to the valley bottom: these may represent an esker deposited by water flowing below the valley ice.

Sea level changes

During the Pleistocene, there were many changes in sea level (Jardine, 1982; Dawson, 1984). Higher stands of the sea are marked by raised beaches, river terraces and rejuvenated river systems. Evidence for lower stands of sea level are not so obvious, but submerged forests and peat bogs and buried river channels have been recognised in some parts of Scotland.

In Arran, the most obvious and widespread of these features is the Main Rock Platform, formerly known as the '25-foot' raised beach. The old name for this feature should be abandoned because it is now known that it varies in height. It is highest (over 14m) north of Loch Lomond and decreases in elevation to near sea level in northernmost Scotland and in northern England. The height distribution suggests a relationship (Sissons, 1976, pp.92, 130; Sutherland, 1984, p.224) between the area of maximum uplift of the shoreline and the ice cap of the Loch Lomond Readvance. Isostatic recovery, after this last ice cap receded, could well account for this raised beach, though the BGS (Browne & Graham, 1981; Peacock et al., 1978) has reported boulder clay on some rock platforms elsewhere in the Clyde area, and considers the Main Rock Platform to be Lateglacial.

A cold climate (perhaps associated with the later stages of the Loch Lomond Readvance) would assist the marine erosion of the hard (Palaeozoic and igneous) rocks. The sea cliffs (often over 15m high) could have been eroded more rapidly if alternating freezing and thawing prevailed in the intertidal zone (Sissons, 1976, p. 129). Several lines of evidence (including radiocarbon dating of pollen sites in the beach deposits) suggest that the Main Rock Platform was abandoned prior to 6,500 B.P., but there is little direct evidence to show that its origin extended back to the very cold climates associated with the Loch Lomond Readvance (which had its peak at 10,500 B.P.). In many Arran U-shaped valleys (e.g. Glen Chalmadale and the lower reaches of Glen Sannox) the stream flows in a distinct notch cut into the base of the 'U'. This rejuvenation of the stream is probably related to uplift of the Main Rock Platform; both events are younger than the glacier ice which shaped the valleys.

It is very clear in the field that the Main Rock Platform shows little sign of any modification by the last glacial event, other than uplift in the region of the ice-caps associated with the Loch Lomond Readvance. The only puzzling field observation is the presence of many of the largest and most obvious glacial erratics on this shoreline (Tyrrell, 1928, pp. 161-2). However, if we accept the theory that the shoreline is postglacial, we may conclude that these erratics subsequently slipped down onto the raised beach from the top of the old sea cliffs. In much of Britain, the cold climates allowed solifluction to take place with alternate freezing and thawing causing the movement of loose material down slopes that are quite stable in our present climate. Such processes would have added greatly to the erosion rates in Arran during the Pleistocene. They might also have aided the movements of the large erratic blocks onto the Main Rock Platform.

In sheltered places around the Arran coast, there are indications of higher shorelines. These mark stands of sea level prior to the last widespread ice in Scotland, but in Arran we have no precise dates. Inland, these older shorelines can sometimes be correlated with river terraces. However, an inspection of Glen Cloy (or the lower parts of any other major valley in Arran) will show that there are more river terraces than there are raised beaches. The river terraces of Arran (like those of the English Midlands) may eventually turn out to provide a fuller record of Pleistocene events than we have at present.

RECENT EVENTS

Although we normally think of Geology in terms of the past, the land today continues to be modified by geological processes. We can learn a lot about the past by observing the erosion, transport and deposition that is going on around us.

One of the most widespread deposits forming today in Arran is peat. Since the onset of temperate (and moist!) climates some 7,000 years ago, peat has been accumulating on flat areas at all altitudes (from the floors of valleys in the south of Arran to the late Tertiary erosion level around the Northern Granite). It is much more widespread (as a thin veneer) than is indicated on the BGS 1:50,000 Drift map of the island (Tyrrell, 1928, pp.266-7, 269).

Much more obviously, river-borne sediments can be studied in the process of transport on every hillside and valley, and in the process of deposition in the lower reaches of the larger rivers and at river mouths. When rivers reach level ground, meanders are usually developed, especially in wide U-shaped valleys. Point bars build up on the inside of the bends, and generally show a fining-upward sequence from gravel to sand; while in times of flood, the alluvial flats between the meanders are covered by finer, silty overbank deposits.

Spits form at the mouths of several Arran rivers (notably in Brodick Bay, Sannox Bay and Catacol Bay). Once the river reaches the sea, the velocity of the current decreases and the sediment load is deposited. The precise distribution of the sediments depends on the direction of the dominant tidal currents and on the prevailing wind directions during storms. Storm beaches were also present along some of the more exposed coasts, where cobbles and gravel have been washed up along the shore. Where there is no nearby river mouth (e.g. North Corrygills NS 034357), the clasts present on these beaches must have originated by marine erosion of the coastal rocks or, possibly, of submerged boulder clay. Also washed up on the shore on most modern beaches are shells and other remains of the littoral and offshore faunas and floras. Just south of Corrygills (NS 044346) there are abundant remains of calcareous algae (*Lithothamnium*) which are growing today on offshore areas with a firm substrate.

Landslides were more common during the Pleistocene glacial periods (Sissons, 1976, p.114), but Arran had a large one about 250 years ago. At An Scriodan (NR 947523), just west of the Cock of Arran, large blocks of Permian conglomerate collapsed onto the shore with a noise that was heard in Argyll and Bute (Tyrrell, 1928, p.267). We trust that all will remain peaceful during your day on Excursion 3!

CHAPTER 4

THE EXCURSIONS

INTRODUCTION

Each excursion is illustrated with one or more geological sketch maps (Figs. 5 to 15) drawn at various scales. The areas covered by the maps are indicated in Figure 1, p.vii. The maps have been designed principally as an aid to finding the localities descibed in the text. They are based largely on the BGS 1:50,000 map (1972 edition), and do not necessarily conform to the 1987 edition.

We have found from experience that each excursion can be carried out in seven and a half or eight hours, inclusive of a break for lunch. We have not presumed to recommend a length of time to be spent at individual localities, as this will vary greatly according to the complexity of the geology, and the needs and experience of those concerned. We have, however, indicated for each excursion a suitable half-way point when lunch might be taken. On alternate excursions, 2, 4, and 6, this occurs conveniently near a pub.

EXCURSION 1

GLEN ROSA

Recommendation: To be done on the first day when weather conditions (and weather forecast) are suitable for climbing the mountains of the Northern Granite.

Note: The formal itinerary set out below has been designed for about three and a half hours' work. After lunch at Locality 11, the afternoon may be spend climbing one or other of the granite mountains surrounding Glen Rosa in small independent parties (each with a map, compass and appropriate clothing; and each having informed the main party leader of their intended route). The itinerary for this excursion concludes with a list of geological features which can be seen on these mountains.

Transport: On foot all day. Starting point: Brodick; end point: Brodick or Corrie or Sannox.

Aims:

To examine:

a) The Stratheden Group (Upper Old Red Sandstone). A thick-bedded sandstone facies, with a problem of determining dip and strike of the beds.

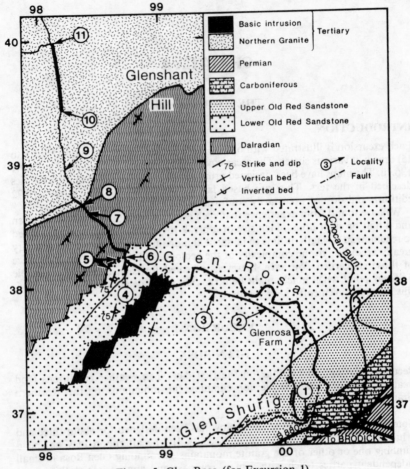

Figure 5: Glen Rosa (for Excursion 1)

b) The contact between the Garvock Group (Lower Old Red Sandstone) and Dalradian rocks. Does this represent a fault, perhaps the Highland Boundary Fault, or is it an unconformity?

c) The metamorphic development of epidote and chlorite in the Lower Devonian, and of cordierite in the Dalradian schists.

d) Pleistocene and present-day geological processes. U-shaped valleys, moraines, jointing in the granite; river terraces; meandering rivers and their deposits.

e) The Northern Granite (60 million years old, Palaeocene). Its mineralogy, grain size and xenoliths; dykes and veins of aplite, felsite, pitchstone and dolerite; its erosional characteristics.

From the junction of the String Road (B880) with the A841, walk west for 150m and turn right along the road to Glen Rosa.

LOCALITY 1 (NS 001369, Fig.5) At the first bridge in Glen Shurig, examine the Stratheden Group (Upper Old Red Sandstone) in the gorge upstream from the bridge, where thick-bedded sandstones are exposed. In general it is not obvious how to determine the strike and dip of the rocks, but examination of the sandstone with a hand lens will reveal the orientation of the detrital grains of mica. In most sediments, the flat mica flakes settle parallel to the bedding, and this provides a means of identifying the bedding.

Detailed examination of the gorge will reveal rare silt and mud laminations within the sandstones, and some horizons with mud flakes, but the strike and dip of the beds can be determined by the orientation of the mica grains alone.

Continue along the road towards Glen Rosa to a point about 100m beyond the gate at Glen Rosa Farm.

LOCALITY 2 (NR 999378) Sit down and look north at the meanders in the Rosa Water. Note the point bar on the inside of each bend in the river. Students should be encouraged to draw a sketch showing where gravel, sand and silt are being deposited (though it may not always be clear that overbank silt and mud have covered the low-lying grassy areas during times of flood). Noting where deposition and erosion are taking place, it may be predicted where deposition may take place in the future, and which deposits are the most likely to be preserved in the stratigraphic record. It should be noted that, while the sequences, in general, fine upwards, there is seldom a continuous gradation from pebbles to mud. Chute channels are present in the field between the road and the river.

These modern river deposits should be compared with the ancient river deposits seen in the Stratheden Group at Corrie and Sannox (Excursion 2). There are important differences, which can be noted and interpreted.

From the same vantage point, observe the river terraces beyond the Rosa Water. The terrace about 20m above the present river level is especially conspicuous. In conjunction with observations made on Excursion 2, consider how the river terraces may be related to the raised beaches on the east coast of Arran. Do the raised beaches and river terraces always occur at the same heights above the present day sea/river levels?

LOCALITY 3 Much of the track to the west of Locality 2 has been repaired using rock seen during Excursion 2. Identify the white mineral. Its diagnostic properties include its cleavage, hardness and density. If you have not yet carried out Excursion 2, name it later.

LOCALITY 4 (NR 986382) The Old Red Sandstone (Garvock Group) rocks exposed on the south side of the Rosa Water are not the usual reddish colour, but are dark green owing to the development of chlorite. Fine-grained, yellow-green coatings of epidote cover the joint surfaces. Generally, the Old Red Sandstone of Arran shows little sign of metamorphism, but from Glen Rosa north-eastwards to Merkland Wood (NS 010399), they appear to have been affected by the Northern Granite. Chlorite is common in low-grade metamorphosed sediments which originally contained clay minerals. Although epidote, a ferric-iron calcium aluminium silicate, can form during low-grade isochemical metamorphism of sediments of appropriate composition, here it appears to have been introduced metasomatically by hydrothermal solutions flushing along joints and through fault and crush zones in this structurally complex area (Friend et al., 1963, p.404-6).

Measure the dip and strike of the beds, in order to compare these with the attitude of the contact between the Old Red Sandstone and Dalradian at Locality 5.

LOCALITY 5 (NR 986383) Leave the track, and follow a contour due west, observing each outcrop to locate the contact between the Lower Old Red Sandstone (Garvock Group) sediments and the Dalradian schists. Numerous small outcrops should enable the line of this contact to be fixed within a few metres, and the contact itself is particularly well exposed in a small ($1m^2$) outcrop about 60m from the river (Plate 2). **DO NOT HAMMER THIS EXPOSURE.** Tracing the contact uphill, it is seen to be offset by a series of small dextral faults.

This contact was, for long, considered to be a continuation of the Highland Boundary Fault. Is it a fault (as shown on the older editions of the BGS map)? Or is it, as claimed by Friend et al. (1963), an unconformity?

A major fault might show:

a) a fault breccia, with fragments both of Old Red Sandstone and Dalradian rocks, or a crush zone, perhaps mylonitised.

b) an absence of bedding in the fault breccia or crush zone.

An unconformity might show:

a) bedding above the unconformity.

b) a basal conglomerate with clasts of a limited number of locally derived rock types, which are all older than the overlying sediments.

c) the dip of the overlying sediments should be approximately the same as the plane of the contact (unless a fossil cliff is being exhumed).

How does the dip and strike of the Old Red Sandstone (measured at Locality 4) compare with the orientation of the contact with the Dalradian?

Examine the Dalradian schists north-west of the contact. The green colour, typical of most of the Dalradian rocks of Arran, is due to abundant chlorite, which was formed from the muddy components of the greywackes during low-grade regional metamorphism in the Grampian Orogeny.

Before descending to the river, look at the terminal moraine straddling Glen Rosa to the east of Locality 5. The river can usually be crossed in the fast flowing section where it is eroding the upstream side of this moraine.

LOCALITY 6 Once across the river, examine the deposits forming the moraine. Are they boulder clay? If not, were they deposited by water? At the south-west end of the moraine, some bouldery beds have a clay matrix; this is boulder clay. Still at the south-west end, the boulder clay is succeeded by parallel bedded gravels; these appear to have been deposited by water. But how can one explain the deposition of the rest of the moraine? It contains many large clasts which are poorly sorted and most of it shows no clear bedding; therefore it cannot have been deposited by water. But there is very little clay left in the matrix, which is mostly a coarse sand. This was probably a boulder clay in which the clay and fine sand components have been removed by fast flowing water, leaving a gravel-rich lag deposit.

Subsequent peri-glacial effects are seen in the top metre of the section, where deformation suggests freeze and thaw action; and thin iron-oxide hardpan stringers are present in places.

Continue up Glen Rosa on the north-east (left) bank of the river across the outcrop of the Dalradian schists.

LOCALITY 7 (NR 984386) Between 400 and 500m from the moraine, polished surfaces of contorted and hornfelsed schists are exposed along the north-east bank of the river (unless it is in spate). Graded bedding normally indicates younging towards the east, but the beds in some outcrops young in the opposite direction and show that some small folds are present. Two small dolerite dykes occur along this part of the river bank.

Many of these rocks close to the Northern Granite have a lilac-blue colour, in contrast to the more usual chlorite green. This unusual colour is due to the development of an iron-rich cordierite by thermal metamorphism near the granite. The cordierite is evenly dispersed in the coarser grained beds, but is concentrated in small dark spots in some of the muddier beds. Biotite is also present in these rocks (although not easily seen with the naked eye); it too is evidence that the Tertiary granite heated the rocks to higher temperatures than those reached during the Grampian Orogeny. Note also that the crystallization of new minerals (including the cordierite and biotite) has resulted in the loss of cleavage in these Dalradian rocks.

LOCALITY 8 (NR 983387) Follow carefully the exposures of the Dalradian schists along the north-east bank of the Rosa Water. The contact with the granite is not exposed, but low on the bank the observed gap is normally about 3m between outcrops, shrinking to about 1m when the river level is very low.

LOCALITY 9 (NR 982389) 300m north of the granite contact, the Rosa Water flows over sub-horizontal granite surfaces, with jointing parallel to the valley floor. Except when the river level is abnormally high, it is possible to wade across the river at several points to examine aplite veins which are clearly exposed on the river bed. Aplite is the commonest rock type in the minor intrusions associated with the Northern Granite. Its mineralogy is the same as the granite (oligoclase, orthoclase, quartz and biotite), but it is much finer-grained. The fine texture indicates that (unlike many granites) the residual magma of the Northern Granite was poor in volatile constituents.

One of the more conspicuous aplite veins has a strike and dip parallel with gently inclined planes of shearing in the adjacent granite. Shearing is present in many other parts of the Northern Granite. It is the result of differential movements within the intrusion after most of the magma had crystallised, but apparently prior to the crystallisation of all the aplite.

LOCALITY 10 (NR 982394) Continue up the east bank of the river to a point where it emerges from a steep, parallel-sided gorge that follows the line of a dolerite dyke (Plate 1). There are some small exposures of dolerite in the gorge near its northern end, but a clamber along the base of the gorge is not recommended. While walking alongside the gorge, note the longitudinal profile of Glen Rosa: the gorge occurs north of a slight step in the valley floor. Ice-excavated valleys do not always maintain as regular a thalweg as do valleys carved by rivers. The gorge has evidently been formed after the melting of the last glacier to occupy Glen Rosa.

LOCALITY 11 (NR 981400) At the north end of the gorge, a waterfall provides an exposure of the dyke (though it is not easily accessible). On a clear day, it will be seen that the dyke is in a direct line with the Witch's Step (Ceum na Caillich on the 1:50,000 map; NR 976443) and is probably continuous with the dyke which has been eroded to form this prominent notch on the skyline (Plate 1).

The jointing in the granite should also be noted. On the valley sides, the joints lie parallel to the hill slopes, while on the hill tops, the joints occur in three perpendicular planes giving a stone-wall effect. Remember that the joints on the valley floor are also parallel to the land surface (Locality 9). So, apart from the crests of the ridges, the joints are related to the modern topography. Some old authorities have suggested that the valley development was controlled by the joint pattern; but it is a bit hard to imagine an ice-sculptured landscape simulated in deep joint patterns prior to the Pleistocene modifications to the geomorphology of Arran! It seems more probable that Glen Rosa was initiated as a river valley before the Pleistocene, very probably along the line of the dyke which now forms the gorge at this point. The joints are thus later features developed by weathering and by the release of load pressure as the valley was progressively eroded, before, during, and since the Pleistocene.

The formal work of the day has now been completed, and this is a convenient place to take lunch.

From this point parties may choose to split up and climb Goat Fell or another of the surrounding granite mountains. It will usually be best if the climbs are made in small groups each going at its own pace, rather than in larger groups. But even in good weather, no individual should ascend by himself, and the leader should know the plans of each group and check that they are properly equipped. These mountains can be dangerous, especially if there is ice on the higher slabs. A'Chir (NR 965420) in particular has claimed many lives, and is best put 'out of bounds'.

While climbing in the granite mountains, the following features should be looked for:

a) Rather rare dykes and veins of aplite, felsite, pitchstone and dolerite, all of Tertiary age.

b) Even rarer, rounded xenoliths of dark, well-baked 'country rock' (probably Dalradian or Devonian).

c) Where a pocket of well-rotted, crumbling granite occurs, note the relative ease with which different minerals are decomposing: – orthoclase (to kaolinite) oligoclase >biotite >quartz.

d) Keen mineralogists might search for topaz and beryl which have been recorded in the Northern Granite.

e) Continue observations on the joint patterns, and in particular, note the way the main joints run parallel to the ridge profiles.

f) When a good vantage point is reached (e.g. the summit of Goat Fell, NR 991416), note how the granite mountains in the east are higher and more craggy than those away to the west and north-west. This suggests that, towards the end of the last glaciation, the eastern mountain-tops projected through the ice as nunataks and were eroded chiefly by frost-shattering, whereas those to the west lay submerged and were smoothed by ice action.

g) Look for signs of glaciation; U-shaped valleys, roches moutonées, corries, etc.

h) In good weather conditions, identify landmarks such as Ailsa Craig, Kintyre, Jura, etc.; sometimes the mountains of Northern Ireland can be seen from Goat Fell. A map covering all of south-west Scotland may be useful.

The best descent from Goat Fell to Brodick is along the 'tourist trail'. Keep to this as you enter the grounds of Brodick Castle, or you will get lost in the dense forests of rhododendron!

EXCURSION 2

CORRIE, SANNOX, AND NORTH GLEN SANNOX

Recommendation: To be done on the first day (if the weather is not suitable for Excursion 1). The Corrie shore section should be done during the period of low tide, and this traverse should be made from north to south, proceeding up the succession.

Transport: Starting point: Corrie; end point: the road bridge in North Glen Sannox. Transport will be needed at the beginning and end of the day, unless resident in Corrie or Sannox. The excursion itself can be carried out entirely on foot, although time can be saved by using transport between Corrie, Sannox and North Glen Sannox.

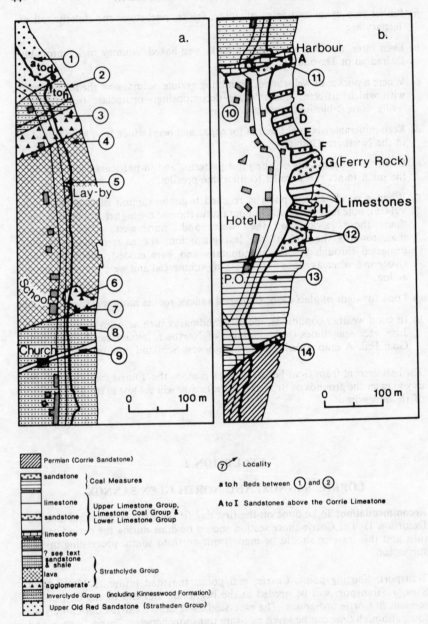

Permian (Corrie Sandstone)

sandstone } Coal Measures

limestone
sandstone } Upper Limestone Group,
          Limestone Coal Group &
limestone   Lower Limestone Group

? see text
sandstone
& shale
lava   } Strathclyde Group
'agglomerate'
Inverclyde Group (including Kinnesswood Formation)
Upper Old Red Sandstone (Stratheden Group)

⑦ Locality

a to h Beds between ① and ②

A to I Sandstones above the Corrie Limestone

Figure 6: Corrie (for Excursion 2)

Aims:

To examine:

a) The Carboniferous section on the shore at Corrie. An olivine-basalt near the base is followed by a sequence of fluvial-dominated deltaic cycles (Reading, 1986, pp. 118, 139).

b) The study of alluvial sediments in the Old Red Sandstone.

c) Pleistocene and Flandrian (= Holocene) geomorphology, including raised beaches, river terraces, corries and U-shaped valleys.

d) The modern gravel and sand spit at the mouth of the Sannox Water.

e) Old baryte workings.

f) The North Glen Sannox pillow lavas and shales, and their relationship to the Dalradian greywackes.

g) The contact between the Dalradian schists and the Northern Granite.

LOCALITY 1 (Fig. 6a) (20m north of the conspicuous conglomerate at NS 023442). Between this point and Locality 2 (100m to the south) examine the section comprising the top of the Stratheden Group and the base of the Kinnesswood Formation. The thicknesses given are only approximate, as the beds are variable owing to channelling and erosion.

a) Cross-bedded sandstones with honeycomb weathering due to solution of the (partially) calcareous matrix.

b) Red siltstone (lm) with green reduction spots, perhaps resulting from the presence of some organic matter, which has reduced the red ferric iron oxide (hematite) coating the silt grains to green ferrous iron minerals. Some calcareous nodules are present in this bed, which indicate evaporation of water within the bed at some time after deposition.

c) Cross-bedded sandstones (3m) showing load structures at the base, especially pronounced where the sands are coarsest. Loading occurs when a bed is rapidly deposited above finer-grained sediments which are still saturated with water. The new deposit than sags down irregularly into the underlying sediments.

d) Siltstone (1.5m) with cornstones. This bed (like bed b) was probably an overbank deposit. The lack of stratification suggests that the silt may have been wind-deposited between river channels. Whilst at times of flood, the sediment would be below the water table, at other times evaporation of its water content would take place, causing the calcium carbonate nodules to be precipitated above the water table. The term 'cornstone' (Allen, 1960), is equivalent to a calcareous caliche in North American terminology. It occurs in regions where the water table fluctuates in level, especially in warm climates.

e) Conspicuous conglomerate (7m) with occasional thin sand lenses, and load structures at its base. This bed was deposited by a fast flowing river that cut and filled a channel in the underlying bed. It contains pebbles of quartzite, vein quartz, schist, green sandstone, red siltstone, coarse iron-stained calcite and dark fine-grained lava (andesite) (Plate 3). Which type of clasts are angular, and which are rounded? Account for the difference. Which older rocks were being eroded? (If you cannot answer these questions now, try again after the days excursion).

Although the conglomerate has a partly calcareous matrix throughout, the top metre of the bed (south of a prominent cleft) is highly calcareous so that the matrix is as resistant to weathering as most of the clasts. This type of rock is known as a calcrete (or, on the BGS 1:50,000 map, where it is given a grey-blue ornament, a pedogenic limestone); it has been formed in much the same way as the cornstones, but the process has continued to the point where the individual concretions have coalesced to occupy all the space between the sedimentary grains. Another example of a calcrete will be seen at Huttons unconformity, (Excursion 3, locality 21).

LOCALITY 2

f) Red and white siltstone with cornstones (1m).

g) Sandstone (1m).

h) Siltstone with cornstones (3m).

Beds e, f, g and h are now assigned to the Kinnesswood Formation at the base of the Inverclyde Group. In the absence of fossils, it it impossible to be sure how close this is in time to the true Devonian/Carboniferous boundary. In Arran, the earliest diagnostic marine fossils in the Carboniferous are of Late Visean age (Locality 10); it is thus probable that all of the underlying Strathclyde and Inverclyde Groups (and possibly the upper parts of the Stratheden Group) are of early Carboniferous age.

Above the Kinnesswood Formation, the remainder of the Inverclyde Group is represented by some thin beds south of Locality 2. These include a mottled shale with signs of burrowing (this may be the earliest marine horizon on the Corrie shore) and cross-bedded sands with some pale green shale clasts.

LOCALITY 3 The succession changes abruptly at this point, to a black, matrix-supported agglomerate with boulders of basalt, some of which are highly amygdaloidal, and rare clasts derived from the Old Red Sandstone; the matrix is dark and fine-grained. This bed defines the base of the Strathclyde Group in the Corrie section.

What are the dimensions of the largest boulders?

Do the clasts occur randomly throughout the bed, or are they sorted?

Can you find signs of bedding?

When you have investigated the above questions, consider the following:

Is the bed likely to have been deposited by wind or by water? Could it be a pyroclastic deposit of airborne debris ejected from a volcanic vent? Or could it be volcanic debris which has been reworked as a mudflow?

Heavy rains are often associated with volcanic eruptions, and mudflows are common on the slopes of many modern volcanoes. We believe that this agglomerate may have been a mudflow, though we have not observed any water escape structures that would help to confirm this view.

LOCALITY 4 The agglomerate is succeeded by a massive olivine-basalt with polygonal cooling joints. The contact is irregular and is best seen above the high water mark, near the grass. Note the phenocrysts of olivine, augite, and much rarer, plagioclase.

Although olivine-basalts usually form thin flows (typically 1 to 5m), there are no clear criteria for distinguishing individual flows for many tens of metres in the lower parts of this unit. It appears either that eruptions followed one another in rapid succession, or that the lava from a single eruption was ponded in a valley to form an unusually thick flow (140m).

Proceed south, looking carefully for indications of the top of a flow, such as red weathering, brecciation, or the concentration of vesicles in the upper part of flows.

Note how the polygonal jointing has been modified by weathering and erosion to form more rounded masses. In places good examples of spheroidal (onion skin) weathering may be studied. Thin veins of fibrous calcite, sometimes with hematite and serpentine, can also be seen.

LOCALITY 5 A large granite boulder, known as Clach an Fhionn, rests on the Main Rock Platform. It is derived from the Northern Granite, and is cut by a vein of aplite (cf. Excursion 1, Locality 9).

Could this boulder be a glacial erratic? Bear in mind that the Main Rock Platform is thought to be 6,500 years old; this is considerably younger than the peak of the Loch Lomond Readvance (at 10,500 B.P.) when Arran had its last ice cap. Consider some alternative mechanisms for emplacement of the boulder, bearing in mind that such boulders are quite common on this raised beach; there are two more between Corrie and Sannox, and another at Corrygills (Excursion 6, Locality 12).

LOCALITY 6 Towards the top of the lava pile there is some clear evidence of the top of a flow: a wedge of volcanic debris is exposed, consisting of recemented angular clasts of basalt and bole (a fine-grained iron-rich oxidised weathering product of basalt).

LOCALITY 7 The weathered material is followed by a massive basalt with abundant rectangular phenocrysts of plagioclase, which is best seen above the high water mark opposite the school gate.

LOCALITY 8 The higher parts of the Strathclyde Group (Lawmuir Formation) are very poorly exposed. Some thin, more resistant beds of homogeneous sandstone, bioturbated in places, project through the cover of beach boulders, but the majority of the lavas, shales and siltstones in this part of the sequence are usually covered.

LOCALITY 9 Try to identify the rock forming the prominent ridge striking towards the sea, opposite the church. The minerals are severely altered and may not be recognisable, and the rock superficially resembles a purple sandstone. The clue to its true identity lies in its texture, which repays careful study with a hand lens. It is cut by some thin veins of calcite.

More siltstones (some mottled) and sandstones (some convoluted) occur towards the top of the Strathclyde Group between the church and the harbour.

LOCALITY 10 Above the road at the harbour, the Corrie Limestone is exposed in a quarry. This is one of a series of quarries excavated in the hillside between the 18th century and the 1914-18 War to obtain lime for the generally acid soils of Arran. The Corrie Limestone lies at the base of the Lower Limestone Group, a sequence of river-dominated deltaic deposits with marine incursions represented by limestones.

Stand back and look at the cliff above the quarry. How many coarsening-upward deltaic sequences are visible?

An idealised deltaic sequence from a text-book might be as follows:

Limestone	Clastic sediment supply ceases (?delta switching) Subsidence causes return to deeper water	start of next cycle

Coal		
Seat-earth with rootlets	Vegetation established	
Sandstone Siltstone	Water shallowing as delta builds seawards; sediment coarsening upwards.	one complete cycle
Shale	Transition from marine to freshwater environment	
Limestone	Marine environment with little clastic supply	

Coal		end of previous cycle

Plate 1. The U-shaped valley of Glen Rosa in the Northern Granite mountains; and Cir Mhor (798m). The Witch's Step, the prominent notch in the skyline (half right), and the narrow gorge in the valley bottom represent the line of a dolerite dyke [Excursion 1].

Plate 2. Contact between the Garvock Group of the Lower Old Red Sandstone (left, south) and the Dalradian (right, north) in Glen Rosa [Excursion 1, locality 5].

Plate 3. Polymict conglomerate close to the Devonian/Carboniferous boundary at Corrie [Excursion 2, locality 1, bed e]. The clasts include vein quartz, quartzite, schist, sandstone, siltstone and andesite.

Plate 4. Gigantoproductus in the Corrie Limestone near Laggan Cottage [Excursion 3, locality 4]. Most of the valves are in the life position, convex sides facing downwards.

Plate 5. The basal Permian rocks on the north-east coast [Excursion 3, locality 12], consisting of interbedded wind-blown sands and parallel-sided flash-flood conglomerates.

Plate 6. King's cave, north of Drumadoon [Excursion 4, locality 14]; one of a series of old sea caves at the back of the Main Rock Platform, carved in dune-bedded Permian sandstones.

Plate 7. View from the north of the Drumadoon sill [Excursion 4, locality 9], a quartz-feldspar porphyry intrusion with well-developed columnar jointing. Its feeder dyke is exposed on the shore in the foreground [Excursion 4, locality 11].

Plate 8. Convoluted flow banding in a pitchstone intrusion on the Tormore shore [Excursion 4, locality 16].

The section above the Corrie Limestone can be interpreted as containing several cycles, each of which in turn contains a greater proportion of coarser sandstone. Deltas are more complex and variable than many older text-books suggest (but see, for example, Reading, 1986, pp. 138-140; Anderton et al., 1979, pp. 148-156).

Although some of the burrowed beds in the Strathclyde Group may have been marine, the Corrie Limestone is the oldest bed in Arran with abundant marine shells. The *Gigantoproductus* (with convex pedicle valves, in life positions, projecting down from the roof of the cave) and other fauna show that it is of Late Visean (Brigantian) age. **IT IS EXTREMELY DANGEROUS TO HAMMER INSIDE THIS QUARRY.** Fossil collecting should not be attempted at this locality; better fossils can be collected much more easily from the Corrie Limestone on Excursion 3 at Locality 4.

Look carefully at the topmost sandstones in the cliff above the quarry. Estimate the dip and strike and determine where on the shore you would expect them to occur. Then cross the road and descend to the foreshore south of the harbour.

LOCALITY 11 How does Sandstone A (Fig 6b) relate to the sequence above the limestone quarry?

For the next 300m the aim will be to proceed slowly southwards to examine further deltaic sequences in the Lower Limestone Group, the Limestone Coal Group and the Upper Limestone Group. As in the cliff above the Corrie Limestone quarry, complete deltaic cycles of limestone, shale, siltstone, sandstone, seat-earth and coal are rare in the Carboniferous of Arran; this is perhaps linked, in part, with the unusually thin Carboniferous sequence here. For example, the presence of several rootlet horizons, suggests that forests may have existed in Arran; the absence of coals at Corrie may well be due to a lack of subsidence to allow the preservation of the wood. The Corrie succession can be regarded as the deposits of microdeltas in coastal lagoons. The thicker sandstones may be related to the influx of higher energy rivers, while the Corrie Limestone and the thin red limestones higher in the sequence reflect marine incursions into the coastal region (H. G. Reading, pers. comm., 1981).

The more prominent sandstones form convenient marker horizons and are labelled A to I in Fig. 6b. The rocks dip at 20° to 30° to the south-east, so we will consider them in order starting above the oldest sandstone A in the north (Locality 11).

South of sandstone A, there is a gap in exposures of about 25m (thicknesses and distances in the following account are only estimates). Then some thin, rippled, red and rusty sandstones and siltstones are seen below sandstone B, a white sandstone about 2m thick. This is followed by 1.5m of red shales and a metre of red sandstone.

To the south of a gap in exposure of 15m, 2m of thin bedded siltstones and sandstones are exposed below sandstone C, a 4m white sandstone. The centre of C contains some cross bedding with siltstone interbeds, and 30cm below the top of C there is a horizon with vertical burrows about 7mm in diameter. On the upper surface of C, *Stigmaria* roots are present. Sandstone C thus shows evidence of high energy currents (the cross-bedding), standing water (the burrowed horizon) and plant growth on land (the roots). It is followed by thin-bedded rippled purple and white siltstones, 0.5m thick.

The next 20m contain discontinuous exposures of thin-bedded rippled sandstones, which lie below sandstone D (1m thick, with a 10cm siltstone interbed). Sandstone D is followed in turn by red shales (1m) and a pink micaceous siltstone with burrows (0.5m). At this point, and subsequently, the following questions should be considered:

How does the petrography of the Carboniferous sandstones differ from that seen earlier in the Stratheden Group (Locality 1)? Do the differences tell us anything about (a) the types of rock being eroded, or (b) the distance of Arran from the region being eroded?

Why are some beds red, some yellow, and some white?

Is there any relation between the colour of a bed and its environment of deposition? (marine, lagoon, river, land). Or its permeability (sands allow water to pass through them more freely than shales)? This is discussed on page 21.

After a gap in exposure of 5m, thin-bedded sandstones (1m) lie below sandstone E, a 1m white sandstone, which is followed by 2m of thin-bedded white and purple sandstones and siltstones with burrows and water-escape structures (which are not always easy to distinguish when the exposures are two-dimensional).

The white sandstone F (2m), forming the slipway north of Ferry Rock shows some fine examples of loading at its base, and contains some water-escape structures internally. Both features suggest very rapid deposition. It is overlain by a pink seat-earth (3m), a compact, fine-grained, leached sandstone with vertical rootlets and larger horizontal roots, including *Stigmaria*.

The white sandstone G (6m) forming Ferry Rock lies to the north of a 30m wide bay with poor exposures. However, at low tide up to three red limestones (each 0.5m thick), interbedded with sandstones and siltstones, may be found. The lowest (most northerly) limestone contains crinoids and the wide gigantoproductid *Semiplanus latissimus*; it correlates with the Index Limestone at the base of the Upper Limestone Group. (It is called the Index Limestone because of its stratigraphic position above the economically important coals of the Limestone Coal Group on the Scottish mainland).

The middle limestone contains productids and minute gastropods, and the youngest is characterised by more abundant bivalves, e.g. *Nucula*.

The white sandstone H (2m) occurs to the north of a second bay (20m wide) which also has poor exposures, but at low tide two further red limestones are sometimes exposed, each with abundant crinoids and brachiopods. The fossils in all these limestones should be examined on the weathered surfaces. **DO NOT HAMMER.**

LOCALITY 12 The white sandstone I (12m) contains some conglomerate lenses, with 3mm grains, near its base. Are the clasts all quartz?

In the central portion of this sandstone, but thinning seawards, siltstones and shales show cross-bedding on a scale that suggests the filling of channels up to 2m deep.

The beds above sandstone I are assigned to the Coal Measures, as they contain non-marine bivalves and plants which indicate a Lower Westphalian age. There are no coals. Proceed slowly up the Coal Measures sequence, noting that the rocks consist of mudstones, sandy shales and thin sandstones. Look for small-scale cross-laminations, slumps, minor unconformities and non-sequences.

LOCALITY 13 Close to High Water Mark, opposite a gate in the wall, irregular structures in the purple and yellow sandstones and shales are present. Are these the results of channel infilling or of rotational slumping?

LOCALITY 14 200m south of the hotel is a prominent white sandstone ridge. Before examining this, search in the red mudstones 8m (horizontally) north of the sandstone for *Anthracosia aquilina*, a fresh-water bivalve of Early Westphalian age. The shells, about 1cm long, are preserved as moulds with occasional dark films accentuating the growth lines; they are found in abundance when the correct horizon is located (Leitch, 1941).

The top of the Carboniferous is taken, arbitrarily, to be the water-laid, highly contorted white sandstone above the fossiliferous mudstones.

Are the contortions due to:-

a) complex folding of the consolidated rock?

b) current drag on unconsolidated sand?

c) slumping down-slope triggered by, say, a seismic event?

d) water escape triggered by, say, a seismic event?

What is the thin, dark rock immediately beneath this sandstone?

Immediately above the white sandstone here, and as far as Largybeg Point in the south-east corner of the island, the sedimentary rocks exposed along the coast are now known as the Brodick and Lamlash Beds and are probably all Permian in age. The local formation here is the Corrie Sandstone. The sandstones are red owing to the presence of hematite. They have rounded, polished sand grains, and large-scale cross bedding characteristics of sand dunes. Pebbles and grains of mica are rare or absent. These sediments were deposited by wind, not water. Note the houses built of this stone. It makes an excellent building material, and was quarried for many of Glasgows buildings until 1928.

Fulgurites – glassy tubes formed as the result of fusion by lightning strikes – have been found in the Corrie Sandstone. They may represent the first unambiguous examples of re-exposed ancient lightning strikes, as opposed to the many fulgurites formed relatively recently at the present land surface (Harland & Hacker, 1966).

All the above part of the excursion can be achieved in half a day, and this may be a suitable time to take lunch.

Drive (or walk) north from Corrie over rocks of the Stratheden Group (Upper Old Red Sandstone).

LOCALITY 15 (NS 019449 Fig.7) At the south end of Sannox Bay the road cuts through a prominent conglomerate bed with unusually large clasts. Examine these

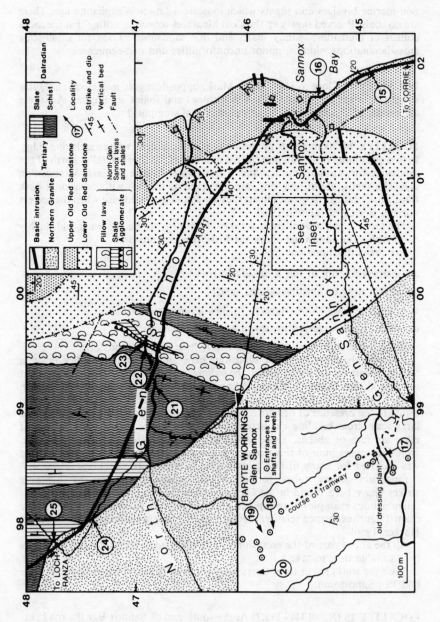

Figure 7: Sannox and North Glen Sannox (for Excursion 2)

carefully and explain why the quartzite pebbles and boulders are better rounded than the other clast types.

Examine the rocks for a few metres north of the conglomerate. These include cornstones in overbank siltstone deposits as at Corrie (Locality 1), fining-upwards sequences indicating channel-fill deposits, and good examples of trough cross-bedding that indicate currents flowing to the east. Mudflake clasts occur in a red pebbly sandstone opposite the south end of the first cottage in Sannox.

LOCALITY 16 (NS 017453) Here the Sannox Water is diverted to the south by a spit before it reaches the sea. The spit demonstrates that long-shore movement of sediment (wave induced?) is chiefly in a southwards direction. Look inland and note the raised beaches and river terraces. These often become confused and difficult to interpret at valley entrances.

Follow the footpath from the road westward along the south side of Glen Sannox to a point beyond the old mine buildings.

LOCALITIES 17 and 18 The baryte of Glen Sannox

The baryte, $BaSO_4$, occurs as veins within fine sandstones and coarse, quartzite-clast conglomerates of the Lower Old Red Sandstone. The sediments in Glen Sannox dip 20° & to 45° to the east and the baryte veins, of which there are at least six, trend approximately north-south across the valley and hade more or less steeply to the west. The veins vary in thickness both horizontally and vertically from up to 2m at the surface, increasing to a maximum of 8m at 30m depth (Tyrrell, 1928, p.271).

The baryte is very coarse-grained in places and the veins are virtually monomineralic; only small amounts of hematite, epidote, calcite and dolomite, and minute traces of malachite having been recorded. It has been deposited hydrothermally from hot, aqueous solutions. Since baryte is relatively insoluble in pure water, these solutions may have been rich in chloride ions and carbon dioxide which increase the solubility of barium salts.

Slickensiding of the baryte, pinching and swelling of the veins, and the presence of xenoliths of country rock within the veins, all suggest emplacement along fault fissures which were active during the mineralisation (Seymour-Smith, 1977).

The age of the baryte is unknown. The Palaeocene Northern Granite, 750m to the south-west, is a possible source, but no mineralisation is clearly associated with this granite pluton, other than the local development of epidote. Dunham (1952) concluded that most of the Scottish baryte mineralisation is probably of Hercynian age.

The Glen Sannox baryte was worked from 1836 to 1862 when ca.600 tons per annum were mined, and again between 1918 and 1939 when a total of ca.60,000 tons were extracted. The adit and shaft entrances and many of the surface installations, including the remains of a water-wheel, may still be seen.

DO NOT ENTER THE ADITS OR SHAFTS. Some are flooded and all may be dangerous. Further details of the workings can be obtained from Shaw (1977).

The ore was sorted and crushed and then conveyed by a self-acting railway to the coast where it was shipped to the mainland for use as a paper filler and for barium chemicals. Nowadays the chief use of baryte is in high-density lubricating slurries for geological drilling.

LOCALITY 17 (NS 007452) Examine anastomosing veins of baryte *in situ* on the south bank of the Sannox Water. Here the mineral occurs as very coarse plates arranged in fan-like fashion, and the country rock is a fine-grained sandstone of the Lower Old Red Sandstone.

DO NOT HAMMER THE OUTCROP.

LOCALITY 18 (NS 006456) A dump provides samples for collecting. Note rare hematite and epidote, and specimens showing slickensides.

LOCALITY 19 The conglomerates forming several crags higher on the hillside are typical of the Lower Old Red Sandstone (Glen Sannox Conglomerate); some 95% of the large clasts being well-rounded boulders of pink quartzite, unlike the conglomerates of the Upper Old Red Sandstone (Stratheden Group) e.g. Locality 15. Identify the remaining clasts. The development of epidote and chlorite around the larger clasts may be the result of thermal metamorphism associated with the Northern Granite.

LOCALITY 20 (NS 003457) Some 150m to the west, a larger crag permits the estimation of the direction of flow of an Early Devonian river (Hint: imbrication).

From here, look westwards and note the U-shaped valley; the change in slope at the granite contact; and the corrie above Sannox.

If you have transport return to Sannox Bay and drive to the bridge in North Glen Sannox. Otherwise contour around the hill in a generally northerly direction and descend to the bridge in North Glen Sannox (NR 992468). En route, measure imbricate structures in further outcrops of Old Red Sandstone conglomerates, and compare your observations with those made at Locality 20.

LOCALITY 21 (NR 992468) Examine the Southern Highland Group (Dalradian) turbidites in the river banks above the bridge. These strike across the river and dip steeply, but do they get younger in an upstream or downstream direction? The answer can be obtained by looking at grading in the rocks. (Hint: the finer-grained, more muddy tops of graded units, generally a metre or two in thickness, show a better developed cleavage. Why?)

These rocks were originally deposited as greywackes from turbidity currents. How does this mode of deposition produce grading?

They have subsequently been regionally metamorphosed to a low grade (temperature less than $400°C$ and pressures less than 5 kilobars), with the development of green chlorite.

Cross the road and proceed downstream.

LOCALITY 22 (NR 995469) Lavas, exposed along the river, have pillow structures, with the convex surfaces of individual pillows generally facing downstream, and concave surfaces facing upstream. This implies younging downstream to the east (Why?), and the lavas therefore appear to overlie the Dalradian metasediments of Locality 21 . The pillow lavas represent submarine eruptions of originally basaltic rocks, now altered to spilite by the conversion of labradorite to albite feldspar, and of pyroxene to chlorite.

The outer zones of the pillows, once glassy, have now devitrified, but zoning is still visible as colour differences.

LOCALITY 23 (NR 995469) The pillow lavas are succeeded in turn by a thin agglomerate and black, pyritic shales, apparently still dipping and younging steeply to the east.

The age of the pillow lavas, agglomerate and shales is now known to be Ordovician (Wheelan et al., in press). However, the presence of downward-facing structures (Johnson & Harris, 1967) suggests that these rocks were affected by some of the overturning which affected the Dalradian beds (see Shackleton, 1958).

If time allows (otherwise the following could conveniently be done as part of Excursions 3 or 4) drive up the hill towards Lochranza and park in the lay-by on the right at NR 979476. Descend to the burn and walk downstream to examine the contact between the Northern Granite and Dalradian schists.

LOCALITY 24 (NR 980474) Note the somewhat finer-grained chilled margin of the granite, up to 1m wide; occasional quartz-rich pods up to 3m beyond the granite; and thermal hornfelsing of the Dalradian within 0.5m of the contact. This exposure is reasonably representative of the Northern Granite margin which, considering the size of the intrusion is unusual in the following respects.

a) Very narrow chilled margin

b) Very narrow thermal aureole

c) Few quartz-rich apophyses invading the country rock

d) Few, if any, xenoliths near the margin, or other signs of stoping (although see Excursion 4, Locality 3)

e) Updoming of country rocks (see BGS 1:50,000 map).

These and other observations lead to the view that during the last stage of emplacement of the granite, it may have ballooned upwards in a largely crystalline state (see, for example, Woodcock & Underhill, 1987).

LOCALITY 25 (NR 978477) The granite/Dalradian contact, now with a generally shallow dip, may be seen again here in a small burn to the east of the road.

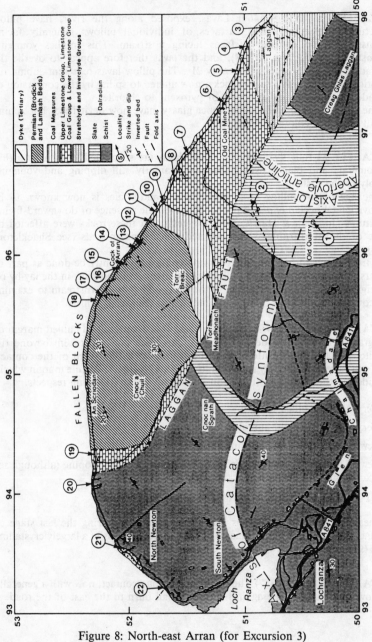

Figure 8: North-east Arran (for Excursion 3)

EXCURSION 3

NORTH-EAST ARRAN

Recommendation: To be done after the Corrie shore section (Excursion 2). Although most of the day is spent along the shore, the state of the tide at any stage of the excursion is not of serious importance. If Localities 24 and 25 were not visited at the end of Excursion 2, incorporate these at the start of the day, while en route to Loch Ranza (or into Excursion 4, see page 63).

Transport: On foot all day. Start and end-point; South Newton (Loch Ranza) (NR939506). If you have your own transport up to mini-bus size, it is best to park at North Newton (NR 932514).

Aims:

To examine:-

a) Loch Ranza slates (Dalradian) in the core of the Aberfoyle anticline – the oldest rocks in Arran.

b) Much of the Carboniferous succession on the northern limb of the Glen Sannox anticline, comparing it with the succession on the southern limb at Corrie.

c) The New Red Sandstone (Permian) of northern Arran

d) Dalradian turbidites

e) Hutton's unconformity; Inverclyde Group (Kinnesswood Formation) on Dalradian

f) Tertiary dykes of dolerite and quartz porphyry

g) Landslipped coastline

From South Newton follow the track eastwards (signpost: Laggan Cottage). After bearing to the left up the hill above the houses, the track becomes a footpath, and good views of Glen Chalmadale are obtained. Notice the incised river along the base of the U-shaped valley. Observe the rounded summits of the granite hills. Why are they so different from the rugged peaks of Goat Fell and the eastern granite hills?

Bear right off the footpath at NR 960507, and head south-east towards an old slate tip (visible from the path at this point).

LOCALITY 1 (NR 963504 Fig.8) The slate quarry beyond the tip heap was worked for roofing slate in the late 18th century, but has been abandoned since 1800 (McLellan, 1985, p. 155). These Loch Ranza Slates are Arran's oldest rocks. They form the core of a major anticlinal fold, the Aberfoyle anticline, which has been inverted into a synform (Shackleton, 1958).

Although the slaty cleavage is obvious, it is very difficult to detect signs of bedding in the quarry face. Look for rare, paler ash bands. A graded bed near the foot of the face demonstrates that the succession is inverted and dips 25° to the east-north-east. The cleavage, probably parallel to the axial plane of the main anticline, dips slightly more steeply in nearly the same direction.

The slates contain rare epidote and pyrite, and detached specimens on the spoil heaps reveal flattened ellipsoids of green material. If these were originally reduction spheres that have been homogeneously deformed during the Grampian Orogeny, then their present volume and ellipticity could provide a measure of the extent and orientation of the deformation.

Walk north from the quarry and rejoin the footpath.

LOCALITY 2 (NR964508) Graded bedding in Dalradian turbidites exposed at the side of the track faces downwards; the beds are inverted.

Shortly beyond Locality 2, the track crosses the Laggan Fault, a major fault (not exposed here) that downthrows to the north-east and juxtaposes the Dalradian rocks of Arran with Carboniferous (and, to the north west, even Permian) sediments.

Continue down the track to Laggan Cottage on the coast. Laggan Cottage is built on rocks of the Strathclyde Group. Older Carboniferous rocks are continuously exposed for some 3.25 km along the coast to the south-east and include basaltic lavas, as at Corrie (Excursion 2).

LOCALITY 3 The first ridge on the shore, 20m north-west of the cottage, is formed of a white sandstone. Lithologically it is identical to the white sandstones at Corrie, consisting almost entirely of well-sorted quartz clasts with little or no feldspar, mica or clay minerals – a truly Arranaceous rock?!

LOCALITY 4 The Corrie Limestone at the base of the Lower Limestone Group (cf. Excursion 2; Locality 10) here consists of alternating 20cm beds of black carbonate, now completely dolomitized (G. Cressey, pers. comm.), and black calcareous shale. Thin, near-vertical joints are partly infilled with calcite; and pale-coloured sphalerite crystals occur in small pockets. Some beds near the top of the 12m thick sequence contain abundant remains of *Gigantoproductus*, some missing their smaller, brachial valves and overturned i.e. they are convex upwards, unlike their orientation when alive (Plate 4). Other fossils include spiriferids, zaphrentids, crinoids, the bryozoan *Fenestella*, and orthocone nautiloids.

The Corrie Limestone is succeeded by several coarsening-upward sequences with a high sandstone/shale ratio, and an absence of limestone. This suggests compensated rates of sediment supply and subsidence. Towards the north-west the beds gradually increase in dip to near vertical.

LOCALITY 5 These near-vertical beds are folded into a shallow syncline that plunges 10° to the west. In the same bay, immediately to the west of the burn, are two sandstones with water-escape structures.

LOCALITY 6 (NR 973513) A hollow to the south of a thick sandstone unit marks the location of a worked-out coal seam dipping 60° to the north-west. Examine the beds above and below this hollow. Is the coal at a point in the sequence which you would predict? (cf. Excursion 2, Locality 10; and Excursion 3, Locality 7). Although the Coal Measures in Arran are barren, the Limestone Coal Group provided one workable seam. This was quarried at outcrop in this hollow, and mined through vertical shafts a short distance to the north-west, during the 18th century. Because of transport difficulties, the coal was burned on the site, and used to heat sea-water to manufacture salt. The old salt pans are still visible (and are indicated on the 1:10,000 Ordnance Survey Map).

A dip slope near the top of the sandstone overlying the coal seam has yielded a remarkable trace fossil. It lies in a small hollow facing the sea, which may have been the site from which the stone was excavated for old buildings nearby. The fossil is a trail of two parallel series of closely spaced imprints, 0.36m apart, and extends for several metres. It has been ascribed to a giant, metre long, myriapod (the group of arthropods which includes the centipedes and millipedes), that had 23 pairs of walking legs (Briggs et al., 1979).

DO NOT WALK ON THE TRAILS OR DAMAGE THEM IN ANY WAY. Photographs of them are best made in bright overcast weather or in the low-angled sunlight of early morning and evening.

What do the trails tell us about the environment of this sandstone? (Footprints on a modern beach get washed away by the next wave; how were these footprints preserved?) The immediately succeeding horizons of seat-earths and shales are rich in plant fragments, and some sandstones bear roots, including *Stigmaria.*

LOCALITY 7 (NR 969515) A north-south trending channel in sandstones looks at first sight like an anticline. Study it carefully, and you will find that many of the different dips and strikes are due to depositional slopes; very little, if any, folding is involved.

The sequence of beds above this channel is listed below. It represents a deltaic sequence close to a textbook example.

Sandstone, coarsening upwards and with a sand volcano (a water escape structure) near the top	3m
Red shale	1m
Sandstone, with rootlets (wedging out to the west)	0.5m
Red shale, with burrows	1m
Sandstone with honeycomb weathering (indicating a partly calcareous cement)	0.5m
Red shale with burrows and thin sandy interbeds	2m
Sandstone, coarsening upwards, with ripples internally	2m
Mottled red shale	2m
Red limestone with crinoids (and covered by grazing trails made by modern gastropods)	1m
Red shale, with desiccation cracks	2m
Sandstone with the conspicuous channel (Locality 7).	

LOCALITY 8 A red limestone in the Upper Limestone Group, possibly the Index Limestone, overlies a white sandstone, and is succeeded by red shale. The

limestone contains productids, spiriferids, zaphrentids, *Caninia* (a rugose coral), crinoids and bright red burrows. Many of these fossils appear to be in life position in lower horizons of this limestone, but in the higher parts, they may have been transported by currents (shallower water?).

After examining the limestones, proceed slowly around the headland until the same succession – sandstone/limestone/shale – is repeated on the shore. The repetition is the result of faulting. Retracing your steps, locate the fault, and estimate its hade, and direction and amount of throw.

LOCALITY 9 (NR 965517) Another red limestone, 70m east of the wall across the raised beach is taken as the top of the Upper Limestone Group.

LOCALITY 10 5 to 10m east of the wall, red mudstones near the base of the Coal Measures contain abundant dark brown spheres of the mineral siderite (variety sphaerosiderite).

LOCALITY 11 10 metres west of the wall, a red sandstone with convolutions due to water-escape, is followed by a white sandstone with large red siltstone clasts.

Examine the Coal Measures for the next 100m. The red mudstones are apparently identical to those at Corrie in which the fresh-water bivalve *Anthracosia* was found (Excursion 2; Locality 14), but apart from plant debris, including *Stigmaria*, no fossils have been recorded from this area.

Find, in this succession, examples of sandstone dykes. These are generally vertical, somewhat irregular fissures in the mudstones infilled by white sand from the overlying (or in some cases, underlying?) beds. The presence of sandstone dykes in this area suggests rapid deposition, trapping water in the sediments which are then disturbed when the water is later squeezed out by the overburden. Leitch (1941) has suggested that the prevalance of sandstone dykes and slumping in the Coal Measures of this section might be related to contemporary movements on the Laggan Fault (see this Excursion, Locality 2).

LOCALITY 12 (NR 963518) The top of the Coal Measures is marked, as at Corrie, by a white convoluted sandstone, and this in turn is overlain, as expected, by red beds of the New Red Sandstone. Unlike the basal New Red Sandstone at Corrie, these sediments are not all dune-bedded; some flash-flood conglomerates occur in parallel-sided sheets (Plate 5).

LOCALITY 13 A prominent dolerite dyke of Tertiary age, running parallel to the shore near the high water mark, appears suddenly to the west of a sandstone bluff. What happens to the dyke at its eastern 'end'?

Follow the dyke, which runs parallel to the coast, for 90 m to the north-west from Locality 13 where it forms a prominent feature.

LOCALITY 14 (NR 961519) Here, immediately to the seawards side of the dyke, the dune-bedded (Permian) New Red Sandstone contains numerous small irregular calcareous nodules, which stand out as 'pimples' on the bedding planes.

Although apparently more concentrated adjacent to the Tertiary dyke near high water mark, we believe that they are of Permian age since they are also present in large clasts in the wadi conglomerate of Locality 16. Perhaps they are mini-cornstones formed near the desert surface after rainstorms?

LOCALITY 15 The vertical sandstone 'walls', produced by the differential erosion of another Tertiary olivine tholeiite dyke, show curious, sub-vertical corrugations. We are unable to offer a fully satisfactory explanation, but suggest that the heat of the intrusion may have caused plastic deformation in the adjacent country rock.

LOCALITY 16 A well preserved wadi conglomerate contains large boulders and smaller clasts of vein quartz, schist, quartzite, white sandstone, dark red and light red sandstone, amygdaloidal basalt, chert, and limestone with productids. Find all these rock types and assign them to older systems.

Many of the vein quartz and quartzite clasts have been clearly recycled; they are well-rounded on some sides and sharply angular on others.

Some of the clasts are in the form of ventifacts. What are these and how have they formed?

Note the shape of the wadi channel and, making allowance for the subsequent tilting of the New Red Sandstone, estimate the original gradient of the channel floor.

LOCALITY 17 (NR 957523) Examine the prominent dyke that cuts across the narrow beach. Its dark colour suggests dolerite at first sight but note the two phenocryst minerals. Noting also that, although as a general rule, acid rocks are lighter in colour than basic rocks, this rule breaks down when acid rocks become ultra-fine grained or glassy. Suggest a name for this rock.

LOCALITY 18 Find occasional disturbances in the bedding of the dune sandstones, best seen in the centre of a 20m long ridge on the shore. These are elongated burrows up to 12cm in depth and 5cm in diameter. Similar burrows can be produced by several groups of terrestrial arthropods (Clemmensen & Abrahamsen, 1983, p.326). Those groups likely to contain genera that had developed a burrowing mode of life by the Permian include scorpions, beetles and spiders.

Westwards for the next kilometre, unless the tide is very low, scramble along the ill-defined path that twists among the fallen blocks of Permian sandstones and conglomerates. Looking at the cliffs above, it can be seen that the dip is to the north-west, i.e. approximately normal to the coast line, and this probably accounts for the rock fall which occurred in the 18th century (see p.36). The coast here faces to the north and is protected by the mainland from the worst of the winter storms. The blocks will thus survive for longer than would otherwise be the case.

LOCALITY 19 Isolated outcrops of a white, unfossiliferous sandstone should be carefully examined with a hand lens. Do you agree with the BGS 1:50,000 map that on lithological grounds these are more likely to be Carboniferous than Old Red Sandstone, New Red Sandstone or Dalradian? Can you give reasons why they are likely to be faulted against both New Red Sandstone rocks to the east and Dalradian rocks to the south and west.

LOCALITY 20 In the vicinity of four closely spaced, north-south trending dykes, the Dalradian turbidites strike approximately parallel to the coastline and dip 35° inland. Good examples of relict cross-bedding and grading may be found, demonstrating that the beds are inverted.

HUTTON'S UNCONFORMITY

LOCALITY 21 (NR 936521) This is one of the most important localities in the history of geology. **DO NOT HAMMER ROCKS OR OTHERWISE DEFACE Nature's work at this place.**

James Hutton (1726-1796), the Scottish geologist, published his 'Theory of the Earth' in 1795, which played a major part in establishing, among other ideas, the concept of 'Uniformitarianism':- in brief, that gradual processes at work today have also operated in the past, and that given a sufficiently long time-scale, they are adequate to account for the complex and profound changes that have occurred during Earth history.

At this locality Hutton first realised, or found confirmation, that the steeply dipping schists represent the products of erosion, transport, deposition, burial, heating and folding, and that to find them now at the surface, unconformably overlaid by unmetamorphosed sediments (themselves of great age) required unimaginably long periods of time.

Apart from its historical associations, the chief interest here lies in deciding where precisely the unconformity occurs (Tomkeieff, 1953).

Dalradian schists dip steeply to the south-east. When traced upwards they are seen to contain vertical fissures filled with sandstone blocks and calcareous cement (calcrete). Some Dalradian fragments have become detached, disorientated and re-cemented. Above is a calcrete bed overlain by the Inverclyde Group (Kinnesswood Formation) containing cornstone nodules.

The Kinnesswood Formation dips gently to the north-west. It was deposited by rivers. Such terrestrial unconformities are usually blurred and confused compared with marine unconformities which are usually sharp and clear cut. Why?

The Dalradian rocks are stained red in this area, probably due to weathering in the late Palaeozoic.

This locality provides a fitting climax to the day's work, but, if time allows, the remaining walk to South Newton affords opportunities to examine the Dalradian further. Examples of grading, cleavage, small-scale folding and vein quartz segregations may be observed.

One more stop, in particular, is recommended.

LOCALITY 22 (NR 932517) A north-west/south-east trending fault is recognizable in the cliffs behind the raised beach. On the shore, a breccia of well-rounded Dalradian clasts occurs a few metres to the north-east of the continuation of the fault. This has been interpreted as a fissure breccia, associated with Late Palaeozoic weathering of the Dalradian land surface; and this and similar fissure breccias and reddening of the Dalradian rocks along the coast and coastal cliffs from this point and to the south-west as far as Dougarie indicate close proximity to the off-shore continuation of Hutton's unconformity (Friend *et al.*, 1970; Harland, 1987).

A few metres to the south-west of the breccia, and as seen looking south-westwards, small-scale asymmetric drag folds in the Dalradian indicate a larger-scale synform inland to the south-east and an antiform beneath the sea to the north-west.

EXCURSION 4

THE WEST COAST: Catacol to Blackwaterfoot

Recommendation: This excursion should be planned with the state of the tide in mind. The Old Red Sandstone/New Red Sandstone unconformity at Machrie (Locality 8) should be visited no more than an hour or two either side of low water; and it is best to avoid high tide during the three to four hours spent along the shore between Blackwaterfoot and Tormore. Thus, if low tide occurs in the early afternoon, the excursion could be carried out as described below. In other circumstances, it may be desirable to visit Machrie out of sequence at the start or end of the day.

Transport: Transport required during the morning. Start point Catacol; end point Blackwaterfoot. On foot during the afternoon. Start point Blackwaterfoot; end point Tormore.

Aims:

To examine:-

a) The Dalradian/Northern Granite contact in the north-west of the island; (and in the north-east if not seen on Excursions 2 or 3).

b) Fold structures in Dalradian schists; and a Dalradian carbonaceous slate facies.

c) A Carboniferous quartz dolerite dyke; and a diorite dyke.

d) The unconformity between the Stratheden Group (Upper Old Red Sandstone) and agate-bearing New Red Sandstone (Permian) sediments on the west coast (the Carboniferous being absent).

e) New Red Sandstone sediments on the west coast.

f) Composite dykes and sills, variously of dolerite, quartz porphyry, felsite and pitchstone, all of Tertiary age.

Drive to Catacol, in the north-west of the island. If, on Excursion 2, Localities 24 and 25 (Fig. 7) were not visited, these can be examined on the way. The

Dalradian/Northern Granite contacts here can then be compared and contrasted with those in the north-west discussed below (Localities 2 and 3).

At Catacol, park to the east of the road, immediately south of the bridge over the Catacol Water. Walk south-east along the south side of Glen Catacol, and bear right up the first burn on the right, the Allt nan Eireannach.

LOCALITY 1 (NR 911487 Fig. 9) Black, graphitic slates exposed in the burn are of Dalradian age and dip 70° to the north-west away from the Northern Granite. This facies probably represents a hiatus in turbidite deposition during which fine-grained sediment accumulated rather slowly. The organic material here is probably derived from marine algae and seaweeds, the deposit pre-dating the time by which the graptolites had adopted a pelagic mode of life. The presence of abundant carbon in shales has been linked with marine transgressions (Leggett, 1980).

On the 1:50,000 geological map, this facies is shown as a continuous arcuate outcrop, 11 km in length, running approximately parallel to the north-west margin of the Northern Granite. It is difficult, but not impossible, to explain the outcrop pattern of the Dalradian as depicted, in terms of a three-dimensional structure. The problem could be discussed as an evening exercise.

LOCALITY 2 (NR 913486) Climb to the conspicuous crag of Dalradian schists above the hut on the camping ground. From here note:-

a) both larger-scale meanders and finer-scale braiding in the Catacol Water.

b) the storm beaches and lagoons in Catacol Bay. Can anything be deduced concerning longshore drift on this side of Arran? (cf. Locality 16; Excursion 2).

c) the different weathering styles and scree colours of the Dalradian and granite on the mountain-side to the north-east.

Ascend the hillside diagonally by the route shown in Fig. 9, stopping to examine detached boulders that show both granite and schist. Although not *in situ*, these show fine examples of the contact.

Features to note include:-

a) chilled margins of variable thickness

b) fine-grained veins and irregular offshoots of granite penetrating Dalradian, sometimes preferentially along the cleavage

c) blocks of Dalradian completely engulfed by granite; these have probably been detached by the process of stoping.

LOCALITY 3 (NR 913483) The granite/schist contact, here *in situ*, is seen to be highly irregular on a small scale, showing a variety of attitudes on a single outcrop. Granite and schist alternately overlie and underlie one another, and there are further indications that the mechanism of emplacement in this part of the intrusion involved a certain amount of stoping.

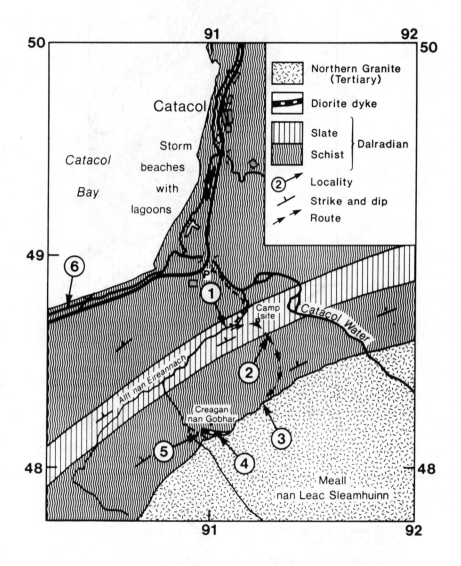

Figure 9: Catacol (for Excursion 4)

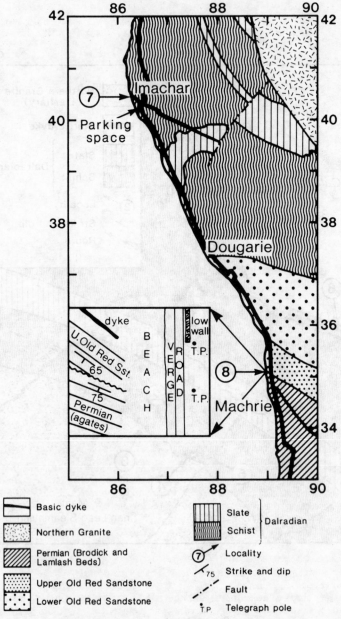

Figure 10: Imachar to Machrie (for Excursion 4)

LOCALITY 4 (NR 911482) A somewhat coarse-grained diorite dyke, intruding the schists but apparently pre-dating the granite, has as its chief minerals dark hornblende and biotite and andesine plagioclase. Unlike the diorites of the Central Ring Complex (Excursion 5), there is no reason to regard this rock as a hybridized gabbro, and it appears to have crystallized directly from a magma of intermediate composition. Its age is unknown.

Outcrops nearby include veins and irregular offshoots of granite.

LOCALITY 5 (NR 909482) Along the line of a small cliff to the north-east of the burn, occasional patches of brecciated, recemented Dalradian schist are interpreted (Harland, 1987) as infillings in fissures in the old land surface that became the Caledonian unconformity (Friend, *et al.*, 1970). See Excursion 3, Locality 22 for further discussion.

Return to transport, and drive south to:-

LOCALITY 6 (NR 903488) Good examples of asymmetric drag folds occur in Dalradian schists along the shore. These may be used to deduce which of the larger, imperfectly-exposed folds are antiforms and which are synforms. When graded bedding is present, use it to determine which way the folds face.

Drive south to Imachar, and after descending the hill to the Main Rock Platform, park by the shore and walk north.

LOCALITY 7 (Fig.10) At Imachar a vertical quartz dolerite dyke (15m thick) is well exposed on the shore (and also in old quarries adjacent to the road). Pink, feldspar-rich veins have a chemical composition (potassium values in particular) that is not explainable in terms of simple differentiation of the parent magma. The veins may have derived, at least in part, from mobilised Dalradian country rock (E. A. Vincent, pers. comm.).

This dyke is considered to be of Carboniferous age; its petrography is very similar to that of the east-west dykes on the mainland, but its orientation is different. Could it have been realigned by the intrusion of the Northern Granite? Drive south towards Machrie.

LOCALITY 8 (NR 889351) On the shore (Fig. 10), the junction between sediments of the Upper Old Red Sandstone (Stratheden Group) and the (Permian) New Red Sandstone is exposed when the tide is fairly low. Rocks of Carboniferous age are absent on the west coast of Arran. In view of the fact that an entire geological system is missing from the succession, the junction is surprisingly difficult to find, since the rocks on either side are coarse red conglomerates and sandstones of fluviatile origin, having similar strikes and dips.

When the junction is located, however, it is seen to be mildly unconformable, the New Red Sandstone dipping somewhat more steeply in a more southerly direction (Fig.10).

The larger clasts of vein quartz and quartzite in the older formation have been reworked, being in part well-rounded and in part sharply angular. Small agate pebbles occur near the base of the New Red Sandstone but not in the Old Red

Sandstone; they are useful aids to locating the contact. If you find an agate clast, work down the succession (northwards) until agates are absent.

Drive to Blackwaterfoot for lunch.

From Blackwaterfoot walk north-west along the coast by the golf course (Fig. 11a). Follow the track across the golf course and along the farm fence towards the coast. After crossing the fence at the stile, take the highest path below the cliff formed by the Drumadoon sill.

LOCALITY 9 (Fig.11a) The Drumadoon sill is intruded into red marls and siltstones of the Auchenhew Beds (Triassic); they much resemble rocks of the Mercia Mudstone Group of England.

The sill itself consists of 30 m of columnar-jointed quartz-feldspar porphyry with large phenocrysts of quartz, plagioclase and alkali feldspar. A 1m thick border of dolerite is present at the base (and top) of the sill. The dolerite contains rounded, resorbed xenocrysts of quartz and feldspar, reminiscent of the phenocrysts in the porphyry. Within the porphyry near its margins are numerous rounded xenoliths of dolerite, identical to that forming the borders. Find examples of all these features of the sill, and then try to explain them. **DANGER: ON NO ACCOUNT HAMMER THE ROCKS AT THE BASE OF THE SILL. IF SAMPLES ARE REQUIRED, THEY SHOULD BE OBTAINED FROM FALLEN BLOCKS ON THE SHORE.**

What follows is a brief summary of a sequence of events which could explain the facts, based on field observations alone (McKerrow & Atkins, 1985), but somewhat elaborated in the light of detailed petrographic and chemical study of the rocks (Kanaris-Sotiriou & Gibb, 1985):-

a) granitic magma began to crystallize slowly at depth to produce large crystals of quartz, plagioclase and alkali feldspar.

b) basic magma, passing upwards through the crust, intercepted the granitic magma chamber. It picked up and incorporated phenocrysts of quartz and feldspar, thereby becoming somewhat hybridised; however, it largely failed to mix because of a viscosity contrast between the two magmas. The basic magma then rose to higher levels, intruding the Triassic sediments, and forming a thin, 2 m(?) thick sill. The phenocrysts, now xenocrysts, were partially resorbed, and the dolerite sill began to crystallize top and bottom.

c) the less mobile granitic magma, with its phenocrysts of quartz and feldspar, was now intruded along the median plane of the dolerite (perhaps the latter had not entirely crystallized, leaving a plane of weakness in the centre of the sill). The xenoliths of marginal dolerite were probably ripped from the partially consolidated wallrock. The acid magma cooled rapidly to form a fine-grained felsitic groundmass.

d) with further cooling, thermal contraction produced columnar jointing, the joints forming perpendicularly to the cooling surfaces of the intrusion.

LOCALITY 10 If the tide is low, an olivine dolerite dyke, striking perpendicularly to the shore, provides magnificent examples of spheroidal weathering.

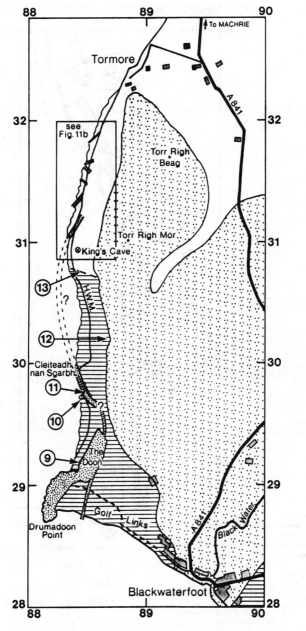

Figure 11a: Drumadoon to Tormore (for Excursion 4)
(For legend, see Fig. 11b, p.70)

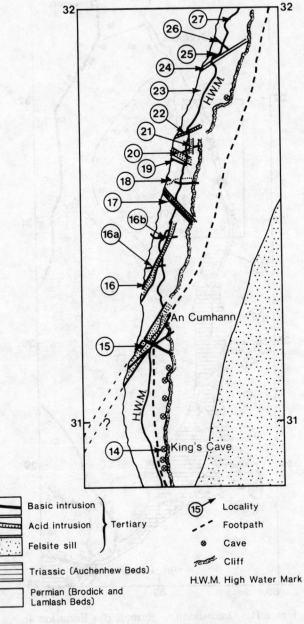

Figure 11b: Judd's dykes (for Excursion 4)

LOCALITY 11 The feeder dyke for the Drumadoon sill runs sub-parallel to the coast (Plate 7). Identify the quartz-feldspar porphyry, and on its eastern side the marginal xenocryst-bearing dolerite (now vertical).

Compare and contrast the composite feeder dyke with the main sill. Relationships are here complicated by (a) a later aphyric dolerite that cuts the quartz porphyry, and is not, everywhere on the outcrop, easy to distinguish from the xenocryst-bearing marginal dolerite, and (b) a buff-coloured, weathered, flow-banded felsite dyke, immediately to the east. This resembles a finely-bedded sandstone, and leaders whose students are without benefit of this guide are recommended to present it as an identification problem.

It is a useful exercise to construct a sketch map of this area, (say 20m x 20m) showing the relationships between the various intrusive rocks.

LOCALITY 12 (NR 886302) The waterfall at this locality is formed by a ledge of sandstone lying horizontally below a sequence of red and green sandstones with some sandy interbeds. The top half metre of the sandstone contains burrows which have been interpreted as arthropod-dwelling excavations in the muddy floors of temporary pools on a fluvial flood plain (Pollard & Lovell, 1976).

Halite pseudomorphs occur on the shore west of Locality 12 (Pollard & Steel, 1978) Cubic halite crystals now replaced by mudstone, suggest extreme evaporation. The trace fossils and the sedimentology have been interpreted in terms of a marginal marine environment (Pollard & Lovell, 1976).

LOCALITY 13 (NR 884307) Note the differences between the parallel-bedded Auchenhew Beds of Triassic age to the south and the massive Permian sandstones (Brodick and Lamlash Beds) to the north. Which would be more likely to accommodate hypabyssal intrusions in the form of sills rather than dykes? What is the nature of the junction between the Permian sandstones and the finer-grained Triassic rocks here?

LOCALITY 14 (Fig.11b) King's Cave (Plate 6) is one of many large caves carved by the sea on this south-west facing coast when the Main Rock Platform was being formed (probably around 6,500 years ago).

Caves in coastal cliffs are relatively rare. Cave formation here is due in part to the massive nature of the sandstones combined with a widely-separated joint system, resulting from the sealing of older joints.

King's Cave is one of several on the coasts of western Scotland where Robert the Bruce is alleged to have watched a spider making several attempts to construct its web. According to the legend, the spider's perseverance and ultimate success inspired Robert to join battle yet again with the English, this time successfully, at Bannockburn (1314). In fact, it seems probable that Robert the Bruce himself probably landed on the east coast of Arran in 1307 after sheltering on Rathlin island (off Antrim). The cave where he studied the spider is thus unlikely to be this King's Cave, although some of Bruce's followers may have used it (McLellan, 1985, p.112-116).

Two different species of the burrowing bivalve *Tellina* have been found washed up on the beach to the north of the cave. One of these species lives today in the Firth of Clyde, but the other is an Arctic species and is probably derived from the Main Rock Platform; about 6,500 years B.C. the climate in Arran would have been a lot colder than it is now, even though the permanent ice caps had gone.

For the next kilometre, the aim will be to examine a famous series of composite dykes, known collectively as JUDD'S DYKES after the geologist who first described them in detail (Judd, 1893).

LOCALITY 15 A 20 m thick composite dyke forms the prominence called An Cumhann, and is best studied on the shore south of the point where the path ascends along a gully. The dyke consists of quartz-feldspar porphyry, again bordered on both sides by narrow quartz and feldspar xenocryst-bearing dolerite, and this is almost certainly a continuation of the composite dyke seen at Locality 11, the feeder for the Drumadoon sill.

Additional complications here include a 1m thick sinuous basic dyke intruded approximately along the median plane of the porphyry; a transverse trench which appears to represent the site of another dyke seen in the cliffs to the east and along which the main dyke has been offset dextrally; and a third dyke that transgresses the south-eastern margin of the main dyke at an oblique angle. Fig.11b, illustrating these complexities, is oversimplified however, and a larger-scale sketch map of the area is recommended as a student exercise.

LOCALITY 16 A pitchstone intrusion striking obliquely to the coast changes its attitude as it is traced northwards. At low water mark its southerly extremity dips 45° inland. Here flow banding in the viscous fluid has been convoluted into tight folds (Plate 8). A thin, spheroidally-weathering olivine dolerite occurs immediately above and below the pitchstone. Midway between low and high water mark **(Locality 16a)** the intrusion is sill-like, its eastern margin dipping only 10° to the south-east conformably beneath a thin-bedded sandstone.

Further to the north **(Locality 16b)** its attitude changes again, and at high water mark it is a dyke dipping 60° inland. Now the bordering dolerite is present only on the seaward side.

This pitchstone intrusion postdates and intersects two minor dolerite dykes, indicated on the map. The more southerly of these variously thickens and thins, wiggles and splits and is bent sharply near its eastern intersection with the pitchstone. The more northerly one has been offset dextrally by the pitchstone and bends to the north-west near low water mark.

The sandstones hereabouts have been much disturbed by burrowing organisms, suggesting the presence of standing water (in lakes or lagoons).

LOCALITY 17 This composite dyke consists of olivine dolerite up to 12m thick, bounded on its northern side by a 1m thick pitchstone and felsite unit. Which of these units was intruded first?

LOCALITY 18 Between high and low water marks two thin dykes, one of dolerite and the other of felsite, cross over. Determine their relationship at the point of intersection. Elsewhere both dykes dip 80° to the south and a narrow screen of country rock intervenes.

LOCALITY 19 An 80cm thick dolerite dyke trends perpendicularly to the coast.

LOCALITY 20 A composite dyke consists of a central 3m thick unit of flow-banded felsite, bounded on each side by a 1 to 1.5m thick olivine dolerite, which is weathering spheroidally. A wedge of pitchstone intervenes on the south side. Account for the joint patterns in this dyke. Why has the dolerite been more deeply eroded than the felsite?

LOCALITY 21 Immediately to the north of the last dyke and above high water mark, a north-south trending pitchstone appears to be a continuation of the pitchstone seen at Locality 16. Its attitude is near vertical, and no dolerite margins are seen. It intersects a 25cm thick olivine dolerite which dips 40° southwards to the west of the pitchstone, is offset 2m sinistrally by the pitchstone, and is vertical to the east of the pitchstone, forming a conspicuous groove in the cliffs above.

LOCALITY 22 A thick pitchstone dips 45° to the south-south-east. It carries small phenocrysts of quartz and feldspar, and has, in places, devitrified to a felsite. Flow banding is seen close to, and parallel to the margins.

LOCALITY 23 The New Red Sandstone sediments here consist of silts and coarse mica-rich sandstones, much disturbed by burrowing. Though some dune-bedded sands are present in the cliffs, the majority of these sediments are water lain. The presence of burrows in parallel beds suggests standing water in lakes and lagoons, rather than river channels. Some of the larger, radiating, burrow-like systems may represent infilled tree roots.

LOCALITY 24 A conspicuous trench marks the site of a deeply eroded dyke. The trench is bordered by ridges of baked country rock more resistant to erosion than the unmetamorphosed sandstones beyond.

LOCALITY 25 Cornstones and desiccation cracks in the sediments provide further evidence of an intermittently wet environment. A vertical section through the thin bed with the desiccation cracks shows infillings of sand between the isolated mudstone polygons. In the process of drying out, the polygons themselves have curled upwards at their edges because of the greater contraction of their upper surfaces (like stale sandwiches!).

LOCALITY 26 A 30cm thick olivine dolerite dyke.

LOCALITY 27 The cliffs at the back of the raised beach consist of New Red Sandstone sediments which are in part water-deposited, but which also include dune-bedded, wind-blown sands.

Continue northwards along the shore, then inland along the track to Tormore (NR 895325).

EXCURSION 5

THE CENTRAL RING COMPLEX

This excursion provides an opportunity primarily to examine a wide variety of volcanic, volcaniclastic, plutonic and sedimentary rock types exposed in the eroded core of a complex Tertiary volcano which underwent one or more episodes of vertical subsidence (caldera collapse). In a single day's field work, however, students should not expect to acquire a full understanding of the structural relationships between the many rock types.

Transport: In the morning transport between localities near the String Road is desirable. Start point: 500m north of Dereneneach (NR 930337) to the lay-by on the String Road at NR 977357. Thereafter, in the afternoon, on foot via Muileann Gaoithe (Windmill Hill), Glen Dubh, and Glen Cloy to Brodick (end point). Alternatively the entire excursion may be made in reverse.

Aims:

To examine:-

a) Tertiary igneous rocks of the Central Ring Complex – rhyolitic agglomerate, felsite, granite, gabbro and intermediate hybrid rocks.

b) Foundered blocks in the Central Ring Complex - Triassic sediments (including marine Rhaetian shales), Lias siltstones and sandstones, Cretaceous chalk and Palaeocene basalt.

c) Pleistocene river terraces and moraines, an esker(?), and the site of a former moraine-dammed tarn.

d) A Tertiary acid sill of spherulitic felsite and pitchstone.

Drive to Dereneneach, and park off the road at NR 930337 (Fig 12a). Walk to the quarry to the east of the road.

LOCALITY 1 Study with a hand lens the fine-grained granite which contains orthoclase, plagioclase and quartz, and lesser amounts of the ferro-magnesian minerals hornblende, biotite and chlorite, less easy to identify. Compare the mineralogy, texture and grain-size of this rock with the Northern Granite seen on Excursions 1, 2 and 4. This granite is fairly typical of several which together comprise the most abundant rock-type of the Central Ring Complex at its present erosional level.

Walk up the north bank of the stream (Allt nan Dris), through a gate in the fence, turn right and find the central one of three burns in the hillside above the fence.

LOCALITY 2 Red siltstones crop out in the stream bed of the southern tributary of the Allt nan Dris. Lithologically these resemble rocks of the Auchenhew Beds of southern Arran, and are probably of Triassic age.

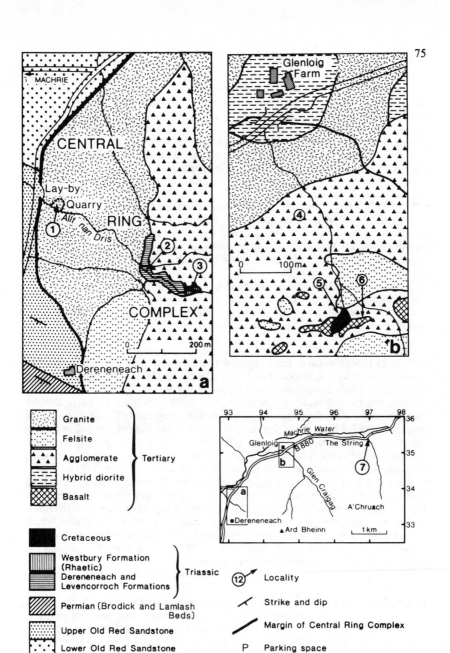

Figure 12: Dereneneach, Glenloig and The String (for Excursion 5)
(chiefly after King, 1955)

LOCALITY 3 Thin limestones and black shales crop out in a small gorge further upstream. The shales yield rare specimens of *Rhaetavicula contorta*, a characteristic Rhaetian bivalve with curved ribs. These late Triassic beds, which may extend laterally beneath the overlying agglomerates, are part of a block which has subsided into the caldera of the Central Ring Complex. For further discussion of this aspect, see p.29 and Locality 5 below.

If you have transport, drive eastwards along the String and park in the lay-by opposite Glenloig Farm (NR 946351) (Fig.12b).

LOCALITY 4 Cross the bridge, and immediately turn left (south) through the first gate, and follow the path up the hill, examining outcrops and loose boulders on the way. In the general area labelled 4 on Fig.12b, these consist chiefly of rhyolitic (felsitic) agglomerate with a variety of clasts set in a fine-grained acid groundmass. This rock is discussed below (Locality 6), after it has been seen there *in situ*.

Deduce the direction of ice-movement in this area during the Pleistocene from the topography on the skyline to the south.

Continue ascending to a small disused quarry on the right of a conspicuous hollow with grassy slopes near the skyline.

LOCALITY 5 Exposures made by quarrying on the west side of the hollow consist of a white calcareous rock below and basalt above. The calcareous rock has yielded Chalk fossils, and the succession appears to be identical to that in Antrim, Northern Ireland, where Cretaceous chalk is overlain by Early Tertiary flood basalts. The chalk has been baked and recrystallized, and it has been quarried here for lime for agricultural use. On the east side of the hollow, where the baked chalk is adjacent to vent agglomerates, there is the development of a narrow zone of skarn minerals, chiefly pale yellow garnets (andradite-grossular), with subordinate magnetite, clinopyroxene and epidote (Cressey, 1987).

The rocks seen here (and in other small patches elsewhere in the Central Ring Complex) make it plain that, in late Cretaceous times, Arran was below sea level. Uplift preceded the Palaeocene basalt lava flows which were erupted subaerially.

Subsequently, central Arran became the site of a volcanic complex which subsided by caldera collapse, causing fragments of Mesozoic sediments and their basalt cover to descend nearly 1000m (King, 1955). Later erosion destroyed the chalk/basalt succession elsewhere on the island.

LOCALITY 6 Excellent exposures of rhyolitic agglomerate are seen in the north-facing cliffs to the east of the quarry. Identify as many clast types as possible. These include: quartzite, vein quartz and schist from Dalradian formations, or from Old Red Sandstone conglomerates; Old Red Sandstone sediments; and Tertiary basalt, felsite, porphyry and granite. Most of the fragments are well-rounded. Some of the clasts may have been rounded in Old Red Sandstone rivers, but in the case of the Tertiary clasts, this has been ascribed to prolonged erosion within the Central Ring Complex prior to their being engulfed in the acid magmas forming the groundmass of the vent agglomerates (King, 1955). The groundmass contains microphenocrysts of quartz and feldspar, and is vesicular in places. Return to the road and drive eastwards.

LOCALITY 7 (NR 969354 Fig.12) A small, unpromising 'exposure' of loose rocks immediately east of the bridge and south of the road nevertheless provides good examples of hybrid diorites. Note, on the BGS 1:50,000 geological map, that the Central Ring Complex contains some areas of gabbro (indicated in purple-E) and of diorite (deep pink-H). These diorites typically show considerable variation in grain size and colour index, and have a hybrid origin. Pre-existing gabbros have been invaded by granitic magmas and partially converted to intermediate rock types. Various stages of the process can be seen at this locality. Darker coloured volumes of rock are still relatively basic; lighter coloured volumes have suffered more extensive hybridisation; veins and patches of pink and white material represent the acid magmas responsible for the hybridization. Hybrid diorites will be seen again later in the day, but this is the best place for a party to familiarize itself with these rocks.

Drive eastwards to the small lay-by at NR 977357. Transport will not be required in the afternoon. Lunch could be taken here, or at the next locality, or at some point on the moor between.

LOCALITY 8 (NR 983351, Fig. 13a) Climb to the summit of Muileann Gaoithe (Windmill Hill – the Gaelic word for 'windmill' is similar to the French 'moulin'. There never was a windmill here but it would be a good site for one!). The hill forms a conspicuous feature as seen from Brodick, and the ridge extending to the east-north-east away from the Central Ring Complex represents a continuation of the Carboniferous rocks seen on the east coast on Excursions 2 and 3. The country rocks near the summit have been intruded by felsites of the Central Ring Complex, and show good examples of flow banding.

LOCALITY 9 On a small flat area, 60m to the south-east of the summit, there is a conspicuous, flat-lying outcrop of bright red siltstones. Lithologically, these are very similar to the siltstones seen at Locality 2 and to rocks of the Triassic Auchenhew Beds of southern Arran. Green colours along joints and small-scale faults are the consequence of reduction of iron by circulating ground waters.

A small (10cm) dyke of quartz porphyry at the southern end of the outcrop contains xenoliths of the red siltstone.

LOCALITY 10 (NR 982350 Fig.13a). Some 200m horizontally to the south of, and 70m vertically below the summit of Muileann Gaoithe sporadic outcrops of brown sandstones contain bivalves and, rarely, Lower Lias ammonites.

These Liassic beds occur topographically below rocks apparently of Triassic age (and with no known Rhaetian rocks between). They must, therefore, either be inverted or exist as separate blocks. In either case, they provide powerful evidence for the violent displacement of Mesozoic rocks during the evolution of the Central Ring Complex (see p. 29).

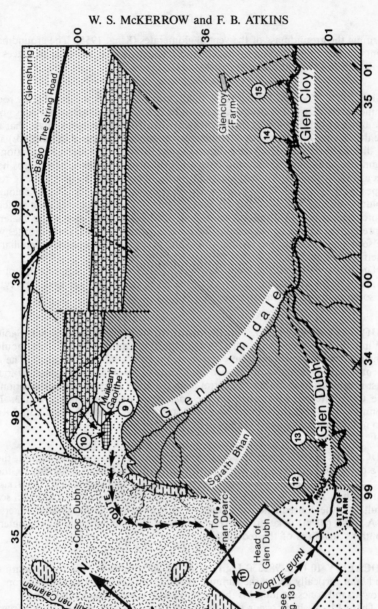

Figure 13a: 'Windmill Hill', Glen Dubh and Glen Cloy (for Excursion 5)
(For legend, see Fig. 13b, p.80)

Walk south-west and then south for about 1km, approximately contouring the slopes towards the shallow col on the sky-line 850m south of Locality 10 (Fig.13a). Although outcrops here are non-existent, occasional boulders and soils suggest granite below.

Proceed southwards from the col for 200m horizontally and 45m vertically and cross a flat boggy area of ground. Continue southwards for a further 200m down a small, shallow valley that slopes gently downwards to the south. Find a convenient outcrop where the party can assemble, and examine gabbro of the Central Ring Complex.

LOCALITY 11 'DIORITE BURN' (Fig.13b) The route now involves a turn to the south-east and a steep descent alongside a small burn. Although the slope is severe, it is safe if taken slowly; there is abundant heather to hold on to, and the only danger is a sprained ankle if the descent is rushed. Unless it is a small one, the party will become strung out, not least because each member should be encouraged to look carefully at available outcrops in and alongside the burn, and identify the rocks as often as possible, as far as the bottom of Glen Dubh, where the party should reassemble.

In turn the following rock types may be found:-

a) Near the start of the descent, coarse-grained gabbro with thin orange weathering crust

b) Felsite

c) Thermally metamorphosed Old Red Sandstone (hard, grey and hornfelsed, but look with a hand lens for original clastic textures)

d) Hybrid diorites showing a variety of grain-sizes and colours (cf. Locality 7), but sometimes fine-grained and grey-green, and easily confused with several screens of epidote-bearing sandstone, which alternate with the diorites. (Hint: crystalline versus clastic textures)

e) Thermally metamorphosed Old Red Sandstone (grey and hornfelsed)

f) Unaltered Old Red Sandstone (red) – near the junction (on the eastern margin of Fig.13b) of 'Diorite Burn' and a larger burn flowing from the south-west.

The party should reassemble at this stream junction. To the east of this point, the Old Red Sandstone and the rocks of the Central Ring Complex are faulted against the Permian Brodick and Lamlash Beds (Fig.13a).

LOCALITY 12 (NR 988337) In the valley bottom at the head of Glen Dubh is a flat oval area of alluvium. The valley was formed chiefly by glacial processes and this area is the bed of a former tarn (small mountain lake), formed after the disappearance of the last ice when the drainage was obstructed by the terminal moraine across the valley. This was later breached, and the tarn drained.

LOCALITY 13 (NR 991338) After crossing the bed of the old tarn, follow the path along the top of the prominent, hummocky ridge running to the north of the river and parallel to the valley bottom. The ridge consists of glacial debris.

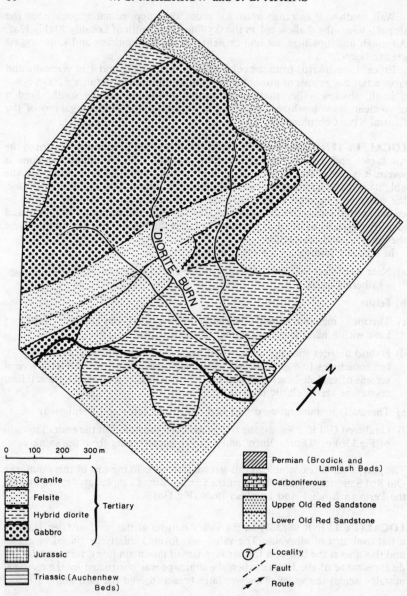

Figure 13b: Head of Glen Dubh (for Excursion 5)
Note: The area of hybrid diorites includes screens of baked
Old Red Sandstone, not shown on the map

Is it a lateral moraine made of boulder clay, or an esker built of sands and gravels deposited by rivers flowing beneath a valley glacier?

Continue down the path, noting the U-shaped valley of Glen Ormidale to the left.

LOCALITY 14 (NS004353, Fig. 13a) This locality is included since it has provided generations of geologists with their first sight, in the field, of devitrification textures. However exposures are now poor and becoming rapidly worse following artificial river diversions in 1982/3. A much better example of spherulitic texture may be seen at Locality 10, Excursion 6, when the tide is low.

In the river bed and on both banks, there are outcrops of a spherulitic felsite sill with narrow margins above and below of pitchstone. The pitchstone is best seen at the base of the sill on the south bank of the river (near the entrance of a small tributary burn). The small (1mm) spherules in the felsite are the result of devitrification of glass around minute crystallites of quartz and feldspar. Probably the entire sill was originally a pitchstone, of which the outer selvages, deficient in crystallites to act as nucleating centres for devitrification, have remained glassy.

Columnar jointing in the sill is perpendicular to the bedding of the Permian country rocks. The dip of the latter is the same as that of the Carboniferous rocks forming the ridge on the north side of Glen Cloy: The structural relations are simple.

LOCALITY 15 (NS007355) Continue down the valley and pause before the first of the houses to study the topography.

The dip slope of the Carboniferous to the north lies in front of Glenshant Hill (NR 990395) where the Dalradian and Old Red Sandstone have been levelled off at about 300 to 400m above sea level. This is a late Tertiary erosion level. Prior to early Pleistocene uplift, the Northern Granite would then have stood up above the erosion surface as a monadnock. In the foreground several river terraces can be seen; they are not as distinct as the raised beaches on the coast, as they slope both down the valley and towards the river and frequently merge with each other.

Continue to Brodick.

EXCURSION 6

SOUTH-EAST ARRAN AND LAMLASH TO BRODICK

Recommendation: The excursion may be carried out in either direction, the state of the tide is not critical, although it is preferable if Localities 3 (near Kildonan) and 7 onwards (between Clauchlands Point and Brodick) are visited when the tide is not at its highest.

Transport: If the excursion is made from south to north, as described below, then transport is needed in the morning. The afternoon is spent on foot along the shore. Starting point: Levencorroch; end point: Brodick.

Aims:

To examine:

a) Wind- and water-deposited sediments of the Permian (Brodick and Lamlash Beds), some with agate clasts, others densely intersected by net veining; a wadi-fill conglomerate.

b) Triassic lacustrine sediments, faulted and intruded.

c) Tertiary sills and dykes of crinanite, quartz dolerite, olivine dolerite, pitchstone and felsite, including examples of basaltic glass (tachylite), flow banding, columnar jointing, vesiculation and various thermal metamorphic effects.

d) Storm beach, coastal lagoon and glacial erratics.

e) Beach deposits of marine algal remains.

Drive to the road bridge on the A841 at Levencorroch (Fig.14) in the south of the island. Parking is not easy, but some of the verges south-east of the bridge are wide enough for vehicles. Follow the path northwards on the west bank of the Levencorroch burn.

LOCALITY 1 (NS 011219) Stop at the flat grassy area where the burn emerges from a narrow gorge, and look up at the hilltops to the east and west. These are built of a thick Tertiary quartz dolerite sill, the base of which is about 30m lower to the west. A Tertiary or post-Tertiary fault along the line of the gorge is inferred.

Fallen boulders provide readily accessible specimens of the quartz dolerite.

On the west side of the gorge, about 40m downstream of the lower waterfall, a dolerite dyke runs parallel to the valley along a fault with sandstones to the west and shales and sandstones to the east. A second dyke, showing excellent development of spheroidal weathering at this point occurs along another fault on the east side of the gorge.

Examine the Triassic sediments (Auchenhew Beds) below the waterfall. Note the parallel bedding and the dominance of clays and fine sands. The lithologies and depositional styles are in marked contrast to the fluviatile, flash flood, and wind-blown sediments of the Permian. However, the absence of marine fossils suggests that the environment was still non-marine. These are probably essentially lake deposits, the presence of desiccation cracks in some beds indicating that the lakes were at times impersistent. Identify the rock forming the lip of the waterfall. Continue upstream to a point 50m above this waterfall.

LOCALITY 2 Observe the dyke on the east side of the gorge. It is a dolerite with variable amounts of plagioclase phenocrysts. Traced upwards it appears to split into three parts. The left-hand, lowest extension of the dyke can be traced as far as the waterfall forming the head of the gorge. Note how the dyke has been displaced by a small fault after its attitude changes towards the horizontal. How does this extension terminate? The central, main portion of the dyke terminates upwards in a shallow dome. The right-hand extension becomes attenuated above a sandstone bed. Sketch a vertical section of the dyke looking northwards towards

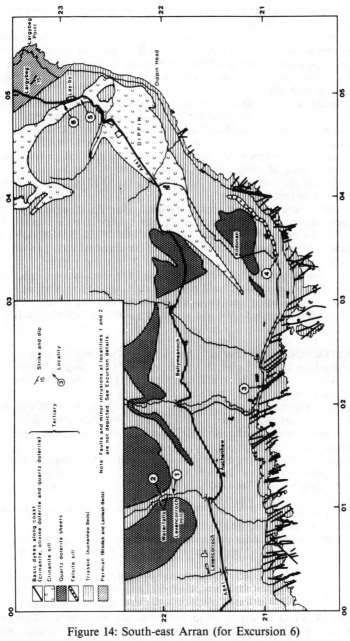

Figure 14: South-east Arran (for Excursion 6)

the head of the gorge. **(Climbing up is dangerous, especially if more than one person ascends at a time).**

It is unusual to observe the upwards termination of a dyke, and this rare example repays careful examination. Low magma pressure is indicated by the sinuous shape and bifurcations of the intrusion and by the way its form is affected by minor lithological changes in the country rock. Baking of the adjacent sediments is negligible.

The sediments themselves show occasional examples of ripple marks and mudcracks; and the fossil footprint of a large reptile (dinosaur?) has been collected here (Specimen G.53 in the Geological Collections, Oxford University Museum).

The sandstones are very rich in muscovite, and some show trough cross-bedding suggestive of crevasse splay deposits which invaded the shallow Triassic lakes.

Account for the fact that the finer-grained, muddier beds are red and the coarser, sandier beds are green.

Examine the geology of the second waterfall. How do the sediments forming the face of the waterfall differ from those to the right. Why is the waterfall there? Notice that the shales by the left-hand extension of the dykes are red except where they have been reduced near joints and below sandstones.

Draw a geological sketch map of the upper part of the gorge.

Discuss the probable northward extensions of the east and west dykes seen at Locality 1; they are probably both present around the upper waterfall.

One and a half hours can be profitably spent at Levencorroch. Return to transport and drive 1km to the east and turn right towards Kildonan (Fig.14).

LOCALITY 3 (NS 022210) Park in a lay-by south of the road, adjacent to a thick olivine analcite dolerite (crinanite) dyke forming a prominent feature on the shore. Why do some dykes stand up to erosion better than the surrounding sediments, while others are more easily eroded?

Account for grain size differences across the dyke. Near the south-west margin of the dyke, a particularly coarse-grained, slaggy zone contains vesicles infilled with the zeolite mineral, thomsonite. The dyke also contains rare xenoliths of leucocratic crinanite.

Although the regional dip of the Triassic sediments in this area does not exceed 5°, they have been locally deformed by the dyke and dip up to 40° away from the intrusion along its south-west margin. There has been an upward component of motion of the intrusive magma at least at this point.

Isolated outcrops of mudstones and siltstones on the beach show desiccation cracks and adhesion ripples.

From an elevated vantage point, note the dyke swarm along the south coast. Compare the density of dykes here with that along the north-east coast (Excursion 3).

Note the view to the south. A quartz-dolerite sill forms the island of Pladda, in the middle distance; and the conical island of Ailsa Craig is visible on the horizon on a clear day. Ailsa Craig is the eroded relic of a plug of riebeckite microgranite, a rock ideally suited for curling stones, which were quarried on the island until recent times. Glacial erratics of this distinctive rock, found in

England, Wales and Ireland, have proved of value in reconstructing the movements of Pleistocene ice sheets.

Drive east along the shore road and park on the verge by a bend to the left.

LOCALITY 4 (NS 034208) Descend the first flight of steps nearest the road and study the vesicles in the vertical section of a felsite sill, exposed at the western side of a broad grassy platform. Try to account for their variable distribution from bottom to top of the sill. Sketch the shape of a typical vesicle. Most have flattened bases and convex tops; and pointed terminations to the south (seawards). Why? Does this tell us anything about the direction of movement of the magma as it vesiculated and then congealed?

The presence of vesicles suggests that the lithostatic pressure exerted by the overburden was relatively low, and that the late Triassic and post-Triassic rocks above the sill were only about two hundred metres thick at the most when the sill was intruded in Tertiary times (Harland, 1987).

Drive to Dippin, and park in the lay-by at NS 050229.

LOCALITY 5 To the south of the lay-by, a small quarry on the west side of the road provides an exposure of the Dippin Sill, one of the larger intrusions in southern Arran. This is another crinanite (analcite olivine dolerite), emplaced in Triassic sediments. Note the coarse grain size; and the analcite, locally abundant as large white patches. A younger dolerite cutting the crinanite is sinuous, of variable thickness, and splits and coalesces near the middle of the exposure to leave an isolated 'island' of crinanite.

The analcite in crinanite and related rocks was formerly considered to be a primary mineral (e.g. Harker, 1954, Fig.45), but a study of the Dippin Sill (Henderson & Gibb, 1977) has shown it to be secondarily derived, probably from nepheline. It seems likely that the analcite in the other Arran crinanites such as the dyke near Kildonan (Locality 3) and the Clauchlands sill (Locality 7) has a similar origin.

Detailed work on the Dippin Sill has also led to the identification of minor units of olivine-free crinanite and two types of basic pegmatite at certain levels; and a hypothesis involving separate pulses of intrusion and magmatic differentiation before, during and after emplacement has been developed (Gibb & Henderson, 1978). The evidence is based on drill core samples and laboratory work, and cannot be demonstrated in the field. However students who have completed a course in igneous petrology are recommended to read the account of this study.

LOCALITY 6 At the roadside opposite the northern end of the lay-by, another 2m thick sill below the Dippin Sill is composed of quartz dolerite, and shows good examples of chilled margins. A vein of basic glass (tachylite) can be seen at the south end of the outcrop.

Drive to Lamlash for lunch.

Drive to the end of the metalled road along the north side of Lamlash Bay (NS 048327). Transport will not be required again if resident in Brodick. Walk northwest along the shore road and then to Clauchlands Point.

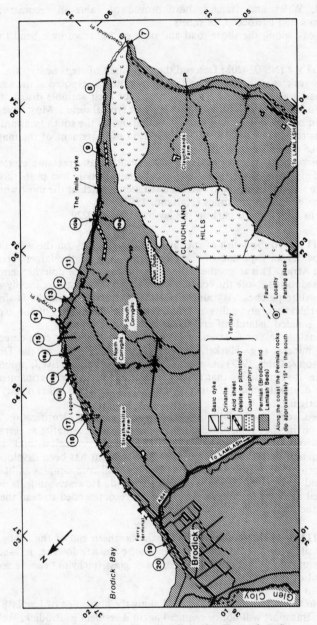

Figure 15: Lamlash to Brodick (for Excursion 6)

LOCALITY 7 (Fig.15) On the south side of the point, near the high water mark, find and examine the upper contact of the Clauchlands Sill, another crinanite. Note the chilled contact and the large, stoped (?) xenolithic block of sandstone incorporated about 2m below the top of the sill. The rocks above the sill, belonging to the local Permian sub-division known as the Lamlash Beds, occur essentially in parallel-sided units, although with occasional cross-bedded units. Some horizons contain quartz pebbles and others have ripple marks.

One silty bed has desiccation cracks. Were these sediments deposited by rivers, or in a lake?

Close to the top contact of the sill, the country rocks have suffered prolonged heating to high temperatures (more than 870°C) and have re-crystallized to a hornfels, with the development of tridymite and diopside, only seen with the microscope (A. Herriot; pers. comm.). The pale amethyst colour of some of the quartz clasts (visible to the naked eye), is also a consequence of thermal metamorphism. The junction with the sandstone is transgressive.

Walk slowly northwards for about 300m across the sill, noting variations in grain-size within the crinanite, and especially the very coarse-grained pegmatite pods, representing concentrations of volatiles. Identify pyroxene (a titaniferous augite), and try to distinguish between the plagioclase and the analcite, which is probably secondary after nepheline as at Dippin (Locality 5). It has been suggested (T. J. Halsall; pers. comm.) that the sill may have been injected in several magmatic pulses, with some settling of olivine between pulses; the more deeply eroded zones representing olivine-rich layers near the base of each zone unit. However tests of this hypothesis await laboratory studies, preferably using drill-core samples.

LOCALITY 8 (NS 056332) The base of the sill shows progressively finer-grained textures towards the contact. Estimate the thickness of this chilled margin. Note the differences in the style of jointing between this chilled zone and the main body of the sill. As at the top of the intrusion (Locality 7), the contact is by no means conformable to the Permian bedding. However, the intrusion considered as a whole is generally sill-like, although Tomkeieff (1961) has suggested that the Clauchlands Sill, and similar crinanites to the west and south of Lamlash (see BGS 1:50,000 geological map) are connected at depth, and form part of a cone sheet complex centred in Lamlash Bay.

LOCALITY 9 (NS 051338) Continue along the coast path until it becomes very indistinct among numerous large elongate boulders of pitchstone, which have fallen from the outcrop of the Corrygills Pitchstone Sill on the cliff above the path. The weathered surfaces of the fallen blocks are the best places to observe flow banding in the pitchstone but it can also be seen *in situ* on the cliff. Many of the flow banding folds are S-shaped, with the folds closing both to the east and the west. Is is possible to determine which way the magma flowed? Note the columnar jointing present both in the Corrygills Pitchstone Sill, and in the Clauchlands Sill on the skyline.

LOCALITY 10a On the foreshore, to the north of a fence, an olivine dolerite dyke splits into two towards the north. At this point, the dyke is cutting fluvial red sandstones and conglomerates. Some of the sandstones show water escape structures, suggesting rapid deposition, possibly in sheet floods. Which way were the currents flowing? Between 100m south and 10m north of the split in the dyke, agate clasts can be found in the conglomerates. Most of them are white with pink or red banding and only a few mm in diameter. How do these correlate with the agates at Machrie? (Excursion 4, Locality 8) (see also this Excursion, Locality 16c).

A good evening exercise is to plot the Permian successions south of Corrie, north of Laggan and south of Machrie. Which is more probable:

1. that the agate horizons at Machrie and Corrygills are the same age (Lovell, 1971)?, or

2. that the appearance of polished desert sand grains (whether in their original sand dunes or derived in water-laid deposits) was more or less synchronous over the whole of Arran?

LOCALITY 10b If the tide is low, find a thick, east-west trending felsite sheet a few metres to the north, and note the excellent development of spherulitic devitrification textures in the pitchstone that forms the lower part of the sheet. Tyrrell (1928) claimed this as "perhaps the finest spherulitic rock in Britain".

DO NOT HAMMER IT.

LOCALITY 11 (NS 044347) A sandy cove (and another further north at Locality 12) contains abundant remains of the calcareous alga *Lithothamnium*. This primitive alga lives in shallow marine areas with a firm substrate off the west coasts of Scotland and Ireland; its robust calcareous skeleton is often mistakenly called 'coral' by local people in these regions. It is seen in several places along the shore on beaches where it has been washed up after storms.

LOCALITY 12 (NS 043349) To the north of the houses at Corrygills, a large granite erratic rests on the raised beach. It contains a vein of an igneous rock you should recognize. How did the boulder get to its present site? (see Excursion 2, Locality 5).

LOCALITY 13 (NS 042350) 40m north of the erratic, a dolerite dyke aligned perpendicular to the shore, has pale, chilled margins. The sandstone adjacent to the dyke has been bleached. There are some puzzling grooves and notches on the walls. How might these have formed? (see also Excursion 3, Locality 15).

LOCALITY 14 (NS 042352) Just north of Corrygills Point, an 18m thick felsite sill crops out on the foreshore. Quartz and feldspar microphenocrysts can be seen with a hand lens in places. The glassy groundmass has partially devitrified to form vague spherulites. As in the Clauchlands and Corrygills sills, columnar jointing is present.

The sandstone above the sill has numerous dark spots. These formed during thermal metamorphism, and consist of aggregates of pyrite and magnetite (now much weathered to limonite). The source of the iron was the red hematite already in the sandstone; the rocks with the most 'spots' have changed colour from red to yellow and white.

At the base of the felsite sill flow banding is visible. Below, there is a 1.5m thick dolerite sill, separated in places from the felsite by a screen of breccia, 0 to 50cm thick. Examine the contacts where the breccia is absent; which sill(s) has (have) chilled margins? Examine the breccia. What fragments does it contain? Can the order in which the felsite and dolerite were intruded be deduced from these fragments? How might the breccia have formed?

From this point to Brodick, the basic dykes repay examination if time allows. Try to distinguish between the oversaturated quartz dolerites which tend to produce smooth weathered surfaces, and the undersaturated olivine dolerites which weather to irregular knobbly surfaces.

Between here and Brodick, the country rocks and some of the dykes are affected by numerous faults, only some of which are depicted in Fig.15.

LOCALITY 15 (NS 041353) Matching offsets at the two margins of a deeply eroded 1m thick dyke reveal that the 'stretching' of the country rocks here in the Tertiary was not perpendicular to the trend of the dyke.

A few metres beyond, note the abrupt change from coarse conglomerates to sandstones. Is this a facies change or the consequence of faulting?

LOCALITIES 16a, b, and c (NS 039354) Find and follow a 2m thick dyke with a slightly curving outcrop sub-parallel to the coast; it dips 70° towards the sea. In two places, 16a and 16c, it is offset sinistrally by faults. In turn it offsets dextrally other dykes (at 16b and 16c) that trend approximately perpendicular to the coast. At 16b note the unusually wide thermal aureole in the sandstones and the development of concentrations of magnetite and pyrite within the aureole to the south-east (cf. Locality 14). Given that the magma was unlikely to have been much above its liquidus temperature, account for the wide zone of metamorphism adjacent to such a relatively narrow dyke. Try to determine the age relationships of the dykes and the faults at these localities.

At 16c, face inland and note the dune bedding in the sandstones forming the cliffs.

The Permian sequence on the east coast of Arran consists of the dune-bedded Corrie Sandstone at the base (Excursion 2: Locality 14), then the dominantly fluvial Brodick Breccia (this Excursion: Localities 19 and 20), and then the mixture of dune-bedded and fluvial deposits seen on this Corrygills section. Clearly the Permian river flood plains of Arran were periodically overwhelmed by wind-blown sands.

LOCALITY 17 (NS 034357) A conspicuous fault has large vertical grooves along the fault plane. Try to account for these. Note the lagoon isolated from the sea by a storm beach. The boulders on the beach include sandstone, dolerite, granite and quartz-feldspar-porphyry. How could they have travelled to this site?

LOCALITY 18 Observe the thin ridges in the sandstones on the foreshore. Find examples of ridges which trace downwards into small faults having offsets usually of only a few millimetres. Thin sections of these fault zones show that the rounded sand grains have been fractured and granulated. The style of these micro-faults appears to be restricted to high-porosity sandstones. When such rocks were stressed to the point of brittle fracture, a small fault developed, which rapidly became slip-hardened, and stronger than the original sandstone. Subsequent stress was then accommodated elsewhere, and the geometry of the total fault system is related to the bulk strain (Underhill & Woodcock, 1987). An analysis of these micro-fault systems in the poorly cemented New Red Sandstone relates the stress to the intrusion of the Northern Granite, and the reactivation of older faults in the pre-Permian rocks (Woodcock & Underhill, 1987). Continue along the shore to Brodick, examining more dykes as time permits.

The following two localities on the Brodick foreshore can be fitted in either on this day or, if resident in Brodick, at any other convenient time, preferably not too close to high tide.

LOCALITY 19 Opposite the Kingsley Hotel, about 10m seaward of the edge of the grass and a wall, two beds of fine muddy siltstone (about 8cm thick) are interbedded with the sandstone and conglomerates of the water-laid Brodick Breccia. The muddy beds show desiccation cracks; each bed extends laterally for only about 10m. They probably represent small puddles existing only temporarily between the channels of the braided rivers that were depositing the coarser beds.

LOCALITY 20 Observe the bedding on the foreshore in the vicinity of the shelter opposite the Gwyder Lodge Hotel. Sandstones and conglomerates of the Brodick Breccia containing a wide variety of pre-Permian and earlier Permian clasts dip approximately 15° to the south; but in a circular area, adjacent to the grass to the west of the shelter, the beds have been broken into blocks showing random orientations.

Walk round the periphery of the area (about 40m diameter), and note the contacts between the blocks and the undisturbed beds. Some of the blocks show signs of plastic deformation; they appear to have been disrupted before they were completely dewatered and rigid, and they have been interpreted as part of the valley walls falling into a fault-bounded wadi (Astin & Macdonald, 1983).

APPENDIX A

FIELDWORK ORGANISATION

Length of Field Course The guide describes six excursions that occupy six days. This is about the right length of time for a beginner in field geology. It allows the student to see most of the interesting features of the island without exhausting his powers of concentration. If six days are not available, we suggest that Excursion 6 be omitted first. For shorter periods, we suggest that those wishing to see a variety of igneous rocks should carry out Excursions 4, 5 and 6; while those wishing to examine sediments should do Excursions 1, 2 and 3. If a field course of more than six days is required, leaders might select additional excursions from the guides by Macgregor (Revised and edited by MacDonald and Herriot, 1983) and Tomkeieff (1961).

Size of party A party of more than 30 students becomes unwieldy. Some outcrops are too small for a larger party to examine simultaneously; on a windy day, the leader's voice may not carry to those at the back; and the single file necessary on many paths entails delays at each stop for the tail end of the party to catch up. Since students require individual direction and encouragement, and should have many questions to ask, the student/teacher ratio should not exceed 15:1.

Travel Arran is served by a regular ferry service (normally 5 sailings daily in the summer) from Ardrossan. Trains from Glasgow arrive and depart from Ardrossan pier to connect with the ferries. Cars, minibuses and larger coaches can be transported on the ferry, though prior booking is advised. Ferry time-tables and bookings can be obtained through: The Traffic Manager, Caledonian McBrayne Ltd., Ferry Terminal, Gourock PA 19 1QP.

The ferry terminal on Arran is at Brodick, which many users of this guide will find the most convenient centre. Local bus services on the island meet each ferry and offer transport to most of the villages and it is perfectly feasible to have a base at Corrie, Lamlash, Blackwaterfoot, Lochranza or elsewhere.

For most of the excursions in this guide, some sort of transport is necessary. Buses, cars and bicycles can be hired on the island. Details of bus time tables and bus hire can be obtained from The Manager, Arran Coaches, Brodick, Isle of Arran.

Brodick also has a large variety of hotels, pubs, shops, banks, etc. and most villages have a pub and a shop.

Clothing Many of the excursions in this guide involve walking over rough ground several miles from the nearest road. Everyone should have suitable clothing, including walking boots with rubber mountaineering soles, loose-fitting trousers, warm sweater and anorak with hood. For the very wet days, a cagoule and waterproof overtrousers are desirable. For the very cold days, take gloves, a woollen hat and an extra sweater. Even when the early morning weather looks set fair, conditions can change quickly within a few hours, and emergency gear (sweater, waterproof clothing and food) should always be carried when more than a few hundred yards from a road. The rainfall averages 46 inches (1168mm) on the west coast, 68 inches (1726mm) on the east coast, and may be as high as 100 inches (2540mm) in the mountains.

Equipment In addition to suitable clothing, the field geologist should have a small, sturdy rucksack, a field notebook, pencil or pen and a hand lens. He will need a topographic (1:50,000) map for finding his way across country, and a geological map to inform him what rocks to look for; even in large parties, it is wise to have a plentiful supply of maps so that if and when small groups get isolated they can find out where they are. A water-proof map case is useful in a region like Arran, where many wet days can be expected at almost any time of the year.

Collecting and Hammering Most young geologists think that they always need a hammer to do their work. This is not necessarily so. A hammer is required to collect fresh rock samples, but collecting is not an essential part of an elementary field course. In general students should be encouraged to use their eyes and brains, not their hammers. Indeed student parties to Arran will find that it suffices if only the leaders take hammers, and this we advocate. Apart from other considerations, the erosion of the island by visitors is a matter of sensitivity to the inhabitants. In any event, rocks should never be hammered without good cause, and under no circumstances should anyone chip the important outcrops visited each year by hundred of geologists. Such activity is nothing short of scientific vandalism. Arran's classic exposures include Hutton's unconformity, the granite/schist contact in North Glen Sannox, and the Old Red Sandstone/Dalradian contacts in Glen Rosa. The famous Carboniferous section at Corrie should be disturbed as little as possible.

Plastic safety goggles should always be worn when hammering or when in proximity to others hammering.

Safety and Behaviour Although we have already mentioned some aspects of safety in the field, we now quote extracts from the advice issued (January, 1982) by the Committee of Heads of University Geology Departments to all students attending geological field courses, on (A) Safety and (B) General Behaviour.

For your own protection, and in the interests of good relationships with local inhabitants, please read this before commencing your field course.

A. Safety

1. Observe all safety instructions given by party leaders or supervisors. Anyone not conforming to the standards required may be dismissed from the field course. Stay with the party, except by clear arrangement with the leaders.

2. Wear adequate clothing and footwear (see above). Leaders may be advised to refuse to allow ill-equipped students on their field courses, since they have a

responsibility to see that students observe the provisions regarding personal safety.

3. Wear safety goggles (or safety glasses with plastic lenses) for protection against flying splinters when hammering rocks or chisels. Don't use one geological hammer as a chisel and hammer it with another; use only a soft steel chisel. Avoid hammering near another person, or looking towards another person hammering (but see above).

4. Take special care near the edges of cliffs and quarries, or any other steep or sheer faces, particularly in gusting winds. Ensure that rocks above are safe before venturing below. Quarries with rock faces loosened by explosives are especially dangerous. Avoid working under an unstable overhang. Avoid loosening rocks on steep slopes. Do not work directly above or below another person. Never roll rocks down slopes or over cliffs for amusement. Do not run down steep slopes. Beware of landslides, or rockfalls from cliffs.

5. Do not climb cliffs, rock faces or crags, unless this has been approved as an essential part of the work. Take great care when walking or climbing over slippery rocks below high water mark on rocky shores. More accidents to geologists, including fatalities, occur along rocky shorelines than anywhere else.

6. Do not enter old mine workings or cave systems unless it has been approved as an essential part of the work. Only do so then by arrangement, with proper lighting and headgear, and never alone. Ensure that someone on the surface knows your location and expected time of return. Be sure to report after returning.

Further advice and guidance is given in the following:

'A Code for Geological Field Work', issued by the Geologists' Association.

'Mountain Safety: basic precautions', published by Climber and Rambler, Perth. PH1 5TT, or 56, Fleet Street, London EC4.

'Safety on Mountains' (1975), published by British Mountaineering Council, Crawford House, Precinct Centre, Manchester University, Manchester M13 9RZ; distributed by Cordee, 249 Knighton Road, Leicester.

B. General Behaviour

All participants in geological field courses, or undertaking independent fieldwork, are expected to observe sensible standards of behaviour, to conduct themselves with consideration for others, particularly in hotels or other accommodation, and not to damage property in any way (e.g. by climbing over walls, leaving gates open, trampling crops).

Please do not disturb the environment more than is absolutely necessary.

Do not collect specimens unless required for serious study.

Do not hammer outcrops casually or indiscriminately.

Do not disturb living plants and animals.

Do not leave litter, including rock chippings.

Observe conservation requirements.

Remember that public access is an acute problem in the countryside and especially in areas designated as National Parks.

APPENDIX B

GEOLOGICAL TERMS

Although most university and polytechnic students who have embarked on their courses should be familiar with many of the terms employed in this guide, its value to amateur geologists and 6th formers will be diminished if their geological vocabulary is limited. For the reader who wishes to prepare in advance, the following words and concepts could, with advantage, be looked up beforehand in any good introductory geology text or geological dictionary.

The list is not comprehensive. A number of terms are defined within the text as they arise; and a few more, used only once or twice, are omitted from the list in the interests of space. Ignorance of these will not seriously handicap the reader's understanding.

Minerals: Magnetite, hematite, pyrite, calcite, baryte, quartz, agate, feldspar, orthoclase, plagioclase, albite, oligoclase, andesine, labradorite, kaolinite, analcite, nepheline, mica, biotite, muscovite, chlorite, pyroxene, augite, amphibole, hornblende, riebeckite, cordierite, epidote, olivine, sphene.

Igneous and pyroclastic rocks: Granite, aplite, felsite, pitchstone, quartz-porphyry, rhyolite, diorite, andesite, basalt, dolerite, tholeiite, gabbro, pillow lava, vent agglomerate, mass flow deposit.

Other igneous terms: Pluton(ic), hypabyssal, magma chamber, feeder, fissure eruption, caldera, stoping, hybridization, chilled margin, xenolith, xenocryst, phenocryst, porphyritic, matrix, variolitic, amygdale, flow banding, devitrification, spherulitic, resorption, vesicle.

Metamorphic rocks: Schist, quartzite, slate, hornfels, mylonite, phyllite, vein quartz.

Sedimentary rocks: Breccia, conglomerate, sandstone, siltstone, mudstone, clay, shale, limestone, chalk, marl, greywacke, turbidite, cornstone, calcrete, seat-earth, coal, mudflake conglomerate, boulder clay.

Other sedimentary terms: Cross-bedding, dune-bedding, grading, younging, channelling, crevasse splay, loading, bioturbation, ripple marks, desiccation cracks, lag deposit, hardpan, clast, ventifact, reduction spot, imbrication.

Structures, etc: Strike, dip, contact, fault, unconformity, non-sequence, anticline, syncline, antiform, synform, hade, drag fold, cleavage, columnar jointing, spheroidal weathering.

Fossils: Algae: *Lithothamnium*
Plants: *Lepidodendron, "Stigmaria"*
Corals: *"Zaphrentis"*
Brachiopods: *Gigantoproductus, Spirifer*
Bryozoans: *Fenestella*
Bivalves: *Anthracosia, Rhaetavicula, Nucula, Tellina*
Gastropods:
Cephalopods: Ammonites, orthocone nautiloids
Arthropods: Myriapods, beetles, scorpions, spiders
Crinoids:

Geomorphology, etc: U-shaped valley, moraine, nunatak, monadnock, roche moutonée, esker, glacial erratic, isostatic readjustment, corrie, raised beach, river terrace, thalweg, meander, point bar, chute channel, overbank deposit, braiding, spit, delta, storm beach, long-shore drift, landslip.

REFERENCES

ALLEN, J. R. L., 1960. Cornstone. *Geol. Mag.,* 97, 43-48.

ANDERSON, J. G. C., 1944. The Dalradian rocks of Arran. *Trans. Geol. Soc. Glasgow,* 20, 264-286.

ANDERSON, J. G. C., 1947. The geology of the Highland Border: Stonehaven to Arran. *Trans. R. Soc. Edinburgh,* 61, 479-515.

ANDERTON, R., P. H. BRIDGES, M. R. LEEDER and B. W. SELLWOOD, 1979. *A dynamic stratigraphy of the British Isles.* George Allen & Unwin, London, 301 pp.

ASTIN, T. R. and D. I. M. MACDONALD, 1983. Syn-depositional faulting and valley-fill breccias in the Permo-Triassic of Arran. *Scott. Jl. Geol.* 19, 47-58.

BAILEY, E. B., 1926. Subterranean penetration by a desert climate. *Geol. Mag.* 63, 276-280.

BAMBACH, R. K., C. R. SCOTESE and A. M. ZIEGLER, 1980. Before Pangea: the geographies of the Paleozoic World. *American Scientist,* 68, 26-38.

BELL, J. D., 1982. Acid intrusions. In SUTHERLAND, D. S. (Ed.) *Igneous rocks of the British Isles.* John Wiley & Sons, 427-440.

BLUCK, B. J., 1967. Deposition of some Upper Old Red Sandstone conglomerates in the Clyde area: a study in the significance of bedding. *Scott. Jl. Geol,* 3, 139-167.

BLUCK, B. J., 1969. Old Red Sandstone and other Palaeozoic conglomerates of Scotland. In KAY, M. (Ed.) *N. Atlantic-geology and continental drift. Am. Ass. Petr. Geol. Mem.* 12, 711-723.

BLUCK, B. J., 1984. Pre-Carboniferous history of the Midland Valley of Scotland. *Trans. R. Soc. Edinb. Earth Sci.,* 75, 275-95.

BLUCK, B. J., 1985. The Scottish paratectonic Caledonides. *Scott. Jl. Geol.* 21, 437-464.

BRIGGS, D. E. G., W. D. I. ROLFE and J. BRANNAN, 1979. A giant myriapod trail from the Namurian of Arran, Scotland. *Palaeontology,* 22, 273-291.

BROWNE, M. A. E. and D. K. GRAHAM, 1981. Glaciomarine deposits of the Loch Lomond stade glacier in the Vale of Leven between Dumbarton and Balloch, west-central Scotland. *Quaternary Newsletter,* 34, 1-7.

CAMERON, I. B. and D. STEPHENSON, 1985. *British Regional Geology: The Midland Valley of Scotland.* 3rd edition. HMSO, London, 172 pp.

CHESHER, J. A., C. E. DEEGAN, D. A. ARDUS, P. E. BINNS and N. G. T. FANNIN, 1972. IGS marine drilling with m.v. Whitethorn in Scottish waters 1970-71. Rep. No. 72/10, *Inst. Geol. Sci.,* 27pp.

CLEMMENSEN, L. B. and ABRAHAMSEN, K., 1983. Aeolian stratification and facies association in desert sediments, Arran basin (Permian), Scotland. *Sedimentol.,* 30, 311-339.

COCKS, L. R. M., W. S. McKERROW and J. K. LEGGETT, 1980. Silurian palaeogeography on the margins of the Iapetus Ocean in the British Isles. In WONES, D. R. (Ed.) *The Caledonides in the U.S.A.* Virginia Polytechnic Institute and State Univ. 44-55.

CONWAY, A., DENTITH, M. C., DOODY, J. J. and HALL, J. 1987. Preliminary interpretation of upper crustal structure across the Midland Valley of Scotland from two East-West seismic refraction profiles. *Jour. Geol. Soc. Lond.,* 144, 865-870.

CRAIG, G. Y., 1965. Permian and Triassic. In CRAIG, G. Y. (Ed.) *The geology of Scotland.* Oliver and Boyd, Edinburgh, 385-400.

CRAIG, G. Y., (Ed.) 1983. *Geology of Scotland.* Scottish Academic Press, Edinburgh, 472pp.

CRESSEY, G., 1987. Skarn formation between metachalk and agglomerate in the Central Ring Complex, Isle of Arran, Scotland. *Min. Mag.,* 51, 231-246.

CURRY, D., C. G. ADAMS, M. C. BOULTER, F. C. DILLEY, F. E. EAMES, B. M. FUNNELL and M. K. WELLS, 1978. A correlation of Tertiary rocks in the British Isles. *Geol. Soc. Lond. Spec. Rep.* 12, 72 pp.

CURRY, G. B., B. J. BLUCK, C. J. BURTON, J. K. INGHAM, D. J. SIVETER and A. WILLIAMS, 1984. Age, evolution and tectonic history of the Highland Border Complex, Scotland. *Trans. R. Soc. Edinb. Earth Sci.* 75, 113-33.

DAWSON, A. G., 1984. Quaternary sea-level changes in western Scotland. *Quaternary Sci. Rev.,* 3, 345-368.

DICKIN, A. P., S. MOORBATH and H. J. WELKE, 1981. Isotope, trace element and major element geochemistry of Tertiary rocks, Isle of Arran, Scotland. *Trans. R. Soc. Edinb. Earth Sci.* 72, 15-170.

DICKIN, A. P., 1984. Provenance of Old Red Sandstone: Pb isotope evidence from Arran, western Scotland. *Trans. Roy. Soc. Edinburgh: Earth Sci.,* 75, 239-241.

DIETZ, R. S. and J. C. HOLDEN, 1970. Reconstruction of Pangea: Breakup and dispersion of continents, Permian to present. *Jl. Geophys. Res.* 75, 493-4956.

DUNCAN, R. A., N. PETERSEN and R. B. HARGREAVES, 1972. Mantle plumes, movement of the European Plate, and polar wandering. *Nature,* 239, 8-86.

DUNHAM, K. C., 1952. Age relations of the epigenetic mineral deposits of Britain. *Trans. Geol. Soc. Glasgow,* 21, 39-429.

ELDERS, C. F., 1987. The provenance of granite boulders in conglomerates of the Northern and Central Belts of the Southern Uplands of Scotland. *Jour. Geol. Soc. Lond.,* 144, 853-863.

ELLIOTT, T., 1974. Abandonment facies of high-constructive lobate deltas, with an example from the Yoredale Series. *Proc. Geol. Assoc. London,* 85, 359-365.

EMELEUS, C. H., 1982. The central complexes. In SUTHERLAND, D. S. (Ed.) *Igneous rocks of the British Isles.* John Wiley & Sons, 369-414.

EVANS, A. L., F. J. FITCH and J. A. MILLER, 1973. Potassium-argon age determinations on some British Tertiary igneous rocks. *Jl. Geol. Soc. Lond.* 129, 419-443.

FLETT, W. R., 1942. The contact between the granites of North Arran. *Trans. Geol. Soc. Glasgow,* 20, 180-204.

FRANCIS, E. H., 1965. Carboniferous and Carboniferous-Permian igneous rocks. In CRAIG, G. Y. (Ed.) *The geology of Scotland.* Oliver and Boyd, Edinburgh, 309-382.

FRIEND, P. F., W. B. HARLAND and J. D. HUDSON, 1963. The Old Red Sandstone and the Highland Boundary in Arran, Scotland. *Trans. Geol. Soc. Edinburgh,* 19, 363-425.

FRIEND, P. F., W. B. HARLAND and A. G. SMITH, 1970. Reddening and fissuring associated with the Caledonian unconformity in north-west Arran. *Proc. Geol. Assoc. London,* 81, 75-85.

GEORGE, T. N., 1966. Geomorphic evolution in Hebridean Scotland. *Scott. Jl. Geol.* 2, 1-34.

GEORGE, T. N., G. A. L. JOHNSON, M. MITCHELL, J. E. PRENTICE, W. H. C. RAMSBOTTOM, G. D. SEVASTOPULO and R. B. WILSON, 1976. A correlation of Dinantian rocks in the British Isles. *Geol. Soc. Lond. Spec. Rep.* 6, 87 pp.

GIBB, F. G. F. and C. M. B. HENDERSON, 1978. The petrology of the Dippin sill, Isle of Arran. *Scott. Jl. Geol.* 14, 1-27.

GREGORY, J. W., 1920. The pr-glacial valleys of Arran and Snowdon. *Geol. Mag.* 57, 148-164.

GREGORY, J. W. and G. W. TYRRELL, 1924. Excursion to Arran. *Proc. Geol. Assoc. London* 35, 401-423.

GUNN, W., 1903. The Geology of North Arran, South Bute and the Cumbraes with parts of Ayrshire and Kintyre (Sheet 21 Scotland). *Mem. Geol. Surv. Scotland,* Glasgow: HMSO, 200 pp.

HALSALL, T. J., 1978. The emplacement of the Tertiary dykes of the Kildonan shore, south Arran. *Proc. Geol. Soc. Lond.,* 135, 462.

HARKER, A., 1954. *Petrology for students.* 8th edition, Cambridge Univ. Press, 283 pp.

HARLAND, W. B., 1987. More Arran geology. *Geol. Mag.,* 124, 175-179.

HARLAND, W. B. and J. L. F. HACKER, 1966. 'Fossil' lightning strikes 250 million years ago. *The Advancement of Science,* 22, 663-671.

HARRIS, A. L., C. T. BALDWIN, H. J. BRADBURY, H. D. JOHNSON and R. A. SMITH, 1978. Ensialic basin sedimentation: the Dalradian Supergroup. In BOWES, D. R. and B. E. LEAKE (Eds.). Crustal evolution in north-western Britain and adjacent regions. *Geol. Jl. Spec. Issue* 10, 115-138.

HAUGHTON, P. D. W., 1988. A cryptic Caledonian flysch terrane in Scotland. *Jl. Geol. Soc. Lond.,* 145, 685-703.

HENDERSON, C. M. B. and F. G. F. GIBB, 1977. Formation of analcime in the Dippin sill, Isle of Arran. *Min. Mag.,* 41, 534-537.

HOUSE, M. R., J. B. RICHARDSON, W. G. CHALONER, J. R. L. ALLEN, C. H. HOLLAND and T. S. WESTOLL, 1977. A correlation of the Devonian rocks of the British Isles. *Geol. Soc. Lond. Spec. Rep.* 7, 110 pp.

HUTTON, J., 1795. *Theory of the Earth, with proofs and illustrations.* Edinburgh.

JARDINE, W. G., 1982. Sea-level changes in Scotland during the last 18,000 years. *Proc. Geol. Assoc. London,* 93, 25-41.

JOHNSON, M. R. W. and A. L. HARRIS, 1967. Dalradian–? Arenig relations in parts of the Highland Border, Scotland, and their significance in the chronology of the Caledonian Orogeny. *Scott. Jl. Geol.* 3, 1-16.

JOHNSTON, T. P. and I. G. MEIGHAN, 1975. The Northern Granite Complex, Isle of Arran. *Proc. Geol. Soc. Lond.,* 131, 331.

JOHNSTONE, G. S., 1966. *British Regional Geology.– the Grampian Highlands.* H.M.S.O. Edinburgh, 103 pp.

JUDD, J. W., 1893. On composite dykes in Arran. *Q. Jl. Geol. Soc. Lond.,* 49, 536-564.

KANARIS-SOTIRIOU, R. and F. G. F. GIBB, 1985. Hybridisation and the petrogenesis of composite intrusions: The dyke at An Cumhann, Isle of Arran, Scotland. *Geol. Mag.,* 122, 361-372.

KING, B. C., 1955. The Ard Bheinn area of the Central Ring Complex of Arran. *Q. Jl. Geol. Soc. Lond.,* 110, 323-354.

KING, B. C., 1982. Composite intrusions.– association of acid and basic magmas. In SUTHERLAND, D. S. *Igneous rocks of the British Isles.* John Wiley & Sons, 441-448.

LEGGETT, J. K., 1980. British Lower Palaeozoic black shales and their palaeo-oceanographic significance. *Jl. Geol. Soc. Lond.* 137, 139-156.

LEITCH, D., 1941. The Upper Carboniferous rocks of Arran. *Trans. Geol. Soc. Glasgow.* 20, 141-154.

LOVELL, J. P. B., 1971. Petrography and correlation of sandstones in the New Red Sandstone (Permo-Triassic) of Arran. *Scott. Jl. Geol.,* 7, 162-169.

LOVELL, J. P. B., 1983. Permian and Triassic in CRAIG, G. Y. (Ed.) *Geology of Scotland.* Scottish Academic Press, Edinburgh 325-342.

MacDONALD, J. G. and A. HERRIOT, 1983. Macgregor's Excursion Guide to the Geology of Arran. *Geol. Soc. Glasgow,* 210 pp.

MacGREGOR, A. G., 1960. Divisions of the Carboniferous on Geological Survey Scottish maps. *Bull. Geol. Surv. Gt. Britain.* 16, 127-130.

MacGREGOR, M., 1965. *Excursion Guide to the Geology of Arran.* Geol. Soc. Glasgow. 192 pp.

MacGREGOR, M., C. H. DINHAM, E. B. BAILEY and E. M. ANDERSON, 1925. The geology of the Glasgow District. *Mem. Geol. Surv. U.K.* 299 pp.

MACINTYRE, R. M., T. McMENAMIN and J. PRESTON, 1975. K-Ar results from western Ireland and their bearing on the timing and siting of Thulean magmatism. *Scott. Jl. Geol.* 11, 227-249.

McKERROW, W. S., 1988a. The development of the Iapetus Ocean from the Arenig to the Wenlock. In HARRIS, A. L. and D. J. FETTES (Eds.) *The Caledonian-Appalachian Orogen.* Geol. Soc. Lond. Spec. Pub., 38, 405-412.

McKERROW, W. S., 1988b. Wenlock to Givetian deformation in the British Isles and the Caledonian Appalachians. In HARRIS, A. L. and D. J. FETTES (Eds.) *The Caledonian-Appalachian Orogen.* Geol. Soc. Lond. Spec. Pub., 38, 437-448.

McKERROW, W. S. and F. B. ATKINS, 1985. *Isle of Arran.* (Excursion Guide, 1st edition), Geologists' Association, 96pp.

McLEAN, A. C. and C. E. DEEGAN, 1978. The solid geology of the Clyde Sheet (55°N/6°W). *Rep. Inst. Geol. Sci.* 78/9, 114 pp.

McLELLAN, R., 1985. *The Isle of Arran.* David and Charles, Newton Abbott. 3rd Edition, 271 pp.

MITCHELL, G. F., 1981. *The Quaternary—until 10,000 B.P.* In HOLLAND, C. H. (Ed.). *A geology of Ireland.* Scottish Academic Press, Edinburgh, 235-258.

MITCHELL, G. F., L. F. PENNY, F. W. SHOTTON and R. G. WEST, 1973. A correlation of Quaternary deposits in the British Isles. *Geol. Soc. Lond. Spec. Rep.* 4, 99 pp.

MYKURA, W., 1960. The replacement of coal by limestone and the reddening of Coal Measures in the Ayrshire coalfield. *Bull. Geol. Surv. G.B.* 16, 69-109.

MUSSETT, A. E., P. DAGLEY, B. HODGSON and R. R. SKELHORN, 1987. Palaeomagnetism and age of the quartz-porphyry intrusions, Isle of Arran. *Scott. Jl. Geol.* 23, 9-22.

PANKHURST, R. J. 1982. Geochronological tables for British igneous rocks. In SUTHERLAND, D. S. (Ed.). *Igneous rocks of the British rocks.* John Wiley & Sons, 575-582.

PATERSON, I. B. and I. H. S. HALL, 1986. Lithostratigraphy of the late Devonian and early Carboniferous rocks in the Midland valley of Scotland. *Rep. Br. Geol. Surv.,* 18, No.3, 14 pp.

PEACOCK, J. D., D. K. GRAHAM and I. P. WILKINSON, 1978. Lateglacial and postglacial marine environments at Ardyne, Scotland, and their significance in the interpretation of the history of the Clyde Sea area. *Rep. Inst. Geol. Sci. London,* 78/17, 25 pp.

POLLARD, J. E. and J. P. B. LOVELL, 1976. Trace fossils from the Permo-Triassic of Arran. *Scott. Jl. Geol.* 12, 209-225.

POLLARD, J. E. and R. J. STEEL, 1978. Intertidal sediments in the Auchenhew Beds (Triassic) of Arran. *Scott. Jl. Geol.* 14, 317-328.

PRICE, R. J., 1983. *Scotland's environment during the last 30,000 years.* Scottish Academic Press, Edinburgh 224 pp.

RAMSAY, A. C. 1841. *Tour in Arran, Glasgow,* 78 pp.

RAMSBOTTOM, W. H. C., 1979. Rates of transgression and regression in the Carboniferous of N. W. Europe. *Jl. Geol. Soc. Lond.* 136, 147-154.

RAMSBOTTOM, W. H. C., 1981. Eustacy, sea level and local tectonism, with examples from the British Carboniferous. *Proc. Yorks. Geol. Soc.* 43, 473-482.

RAMSBOTTOM, W. H. C., M. A. CALVER, R. M. C. EAGER, F. HODSON, D. W. HOLLIDAY, C. J. STUBBLEFIELD and R. B. WILSON, 1978. A correlation of Silesian rocks in the British Isles. *Geol. Soc. Lond. Spec. Rep.* 10, 81 pp.

READ, W. A., 1969. Fluviatile deposits in Namurian rocks of Central Scotland. *Geol. Mag.* 106, 331-347.

READING, H. G. (Ed.), 1986. *Sedimentary environments and facies.* 2nd Edition. Blackwell Scientific Publications, Oxford, 615 pp.

RICHEY, J. E., 1961. *British Regional Geology.—Scotland, the Tertiary Volcanic Districts.* (3rd ed.) H.M.S.O. Edinburgh, 120 pp.

SCOTESE, C. R., R. K. BAMBACH, C. BARTON, R. VAN DER VOO and A. M. ZIEGLER, 1979. Paleozoic base maps. *Jl. Geol.*, 87, 217-277.

SEYMOUR-SMITH, S., 1977. A visit to the Glen Sannox baryte mine, Isle of Arran. *Russell Soc. Newsletter No.* 4, 23-26.

SHACKLETON, R. M., 1958. Downward-facing structures of the Highland Border. *Q. Jl. Geol. Soc. Lond.*, 108, 361-392.

SHAW, R. P., 1977. Arran barytes mine, Glen Sannox, Isle of Arran. *Bull. Peak District Mines Historical Soc.*, 6, 209-217.

SISSONS, J. B., 1976. *Scotland*, Methuen, London. 150 pp.

SISSONS, J. B., 1981. British shore platforms and ice-sheets. *Nature*, 291, 473-475.

SMITH, D. B., R. G. W. BRUNSTROM, P. I. MANNING, S. SIMPSON and F. W. SHOTTON, 1974. A correlation of Permian rocks in the British Isles. *Geol. Soc. Lond. Spec. Rep.* 5, 45 pp.

SNELLING, N. J. (Ed.) 1985. *The chronology of the geological record.* Geological Society London, Memoir 10, 343p.

SPEIGHT, J. M., R. R. SKELHORN, T. SLOAN and R. J. KNAPP, 1982. The dyke swarms of Scotland. In SUTHERLAND, D. S. *Igneous rocks of the British Isles.* John Wiley & Sons. 449-459.

SUTHERLAND, D. G., 1984. The Quaternary deposits and landforms of Scotland and the neighbouring shelves: A review. *Quaternary Science Reviews*, 3, 157-254.

SUTHERLAND, D. S. (Ed.), 1982. *Igneous rocks of the British Isles.* John Wiley & Sons, 645 pp.

THOMPSON, R. N., 1982. Geochemistry and magma genesis. in SUTHERLAND, D. S. (Ed.). *Igneous rocks of the British Isles.* John Wiley & Sons, 461-478.

TOMKEIEFF, S. I., 1953. 'Hutton's unconformity', Isle of Arran. *Geol. Mag.*, 90, 404-408.

TOMKEIEFF, S. I., 1961. Isle of Arran. No.32 in Excursion Guide Series. *Geologists' Association* 33pp.

TYRRELL, G. W., 1928. The geology of Arran. *Mem. Geol. Surv. U.K.* 292 pp. (2nd impression issued by the British Geological Survey, 1987)

UNDERHILL, J. R. and N. H. WOODCOCK, 1987. Faulting mechanisms in high-porosity sandstones; New Red Sandstone, Arran, Scotland. In JONES, M. E. and R. M. F. PRESTON (Eds.), Deformation of sediments and sedimentary rocks, *Geol. Soc. Spec. Public.* 29, 91-105.

UPTON, B. J. G., P. ASPEN, and N. A. CHAPMAN, 1983. The upper mantle and deep crust beneath the British Isles: evidence from inclusions in volcanic rocks. *Jour. Geol. Soc. Lond.*, 140, 105-121.

WARRINGTON, G., M. G. AUDLEY-CHARLES, R. E. ELLIOTT, W. B. EVANS, H. C. IVIMEY-COOK, P. E. KENT, P. L. ROBINSON, F. W. SHOTTON and F. M. TAYLOR, 1980. A correlation of Triassic rocks in the British Isles. *Geol. Soc. Lond. Spec. Rep.* 13, 78 pp.

WHEELAN, G. M., B. J. BLUCK and G. J. BURTON A preliminary stratigraphy for the Highland Border Complex. *Scott. J. Geol.* (in prep.)

WILSON, H. E., 1972. *Regional geology of Northern Ireland.* H.M.S.O. Belfast. 115 pp.

WOODCOCK, N. H. and J. R. UNDERHILL, 1987. Emplacement-related fault patterns around the Northern Granite, Arran, Scotland. *Bull. Geol. Soc. Amer.*, 98, 515-527.

INDEX

Page numbers **37** *et seq*. refer to the excursions

Dolerite: *see* composite intrusions; dykes; sills
Drumadoon: *see* sills
Dune-bedding, 22-23, 51, 60-61, 71, 73
Dykes, 25-31
  Imachar, 10, 22, 67
  Judd's, 30, 72-73
  Kildonan, 84
  Levencorroch, 82-84
  swarms, 25, 30-31, 84, 89

Epidote, 27, 40, 53, 54, 76, 79

Felsite, 10, 26, 30, 71-73, 76-78, 81, 85, 88-89
Fulgurites, 23, 51

Gabbro, 26, 29, 77, 79
Glen Rosa, 33, 37-43
Glen Sannox, 53-54
Goat Fell, 27, 34, 42-43, 57
Grampian Orogeny, 13-15, 41, 58

Hercynian Orogeny, 10, 13, 22, 53
Highland Boundary Fault 1, 4-5, 8, 11-16, 28, 40
Hornfels, 41, 55, 79, 87
Holy Island, 10, 26, 31
Hutton's Unconformity, 16, 62
Hybrid igneous rocks, 26, 29, 77, 79

Imachar: *see* dykes
Inverclyde Group: *see* Carboniferous

Judd's dykes: *see* dykes
Jurassic, 13, 24-25, 29, 77

Kildonan, 84-85
King's Cave, 71
Kintyre, 4-5, 20, 33, 43

Laggan, 21-22, 57-58
Lamlash, 23-24, 30, 85
Levencorroch, 24, 30, 82-84
Limestone Coal Group: *see* Carboniferous
Lochranza, 14, 57
Lower Limestone Group: *see* Carboniferous

Machrie, 23, 66-68, 88
Metamorphism, 11, 14, 39-41, 54-55, 73, 76, 79, 87, 89
Midland Valley of Scotland, 1, 10, 15-22

New Red Sandstone: *see* Permian
North Glen Sannox, 8, 13-15, 54-55
Northern Granite, 5-8, 12, 26-28, 32-34, 41-43, 53, 55, 64-67